"Jake, Please, What Are You Doing?

Wait, you must stop."

Raising his head, Jake gazed down at her, his hand still resting on her breast. The expression in his eyes was one of wariness and grim uncertainty. "That was my fault. I had no business taking advantage of you that way, Sabrina. For God's sake, I'm supposed to be protecting you!" He hesitated and then asked with a hint of challenge, "Are you going to stage a major scene? Tell me I obviously can't be trusted as a bodyguard?"

Sabrina tried to gather her wits. "Can I?"

"Can you what?" he retorted huskily.

"Trust you as a bodyguard?"

STEPHANIE JAMES

readily admits that the chief influence on her writing is her "lifelong addiction to romantic daydreaming." She has spent the last nine years living and working with her engineer husband in a wide variety of places, including the Caribbean, the Southeast, and the Pacific Northwest. Ms. James currently resides in California.

Dear Reader:

SILHOUETTE DESIRE is an exciting new line of contemporary romances from Silhouette Books. During the past year, many Silhouette readers have written in telling us what other types of stories they'd like to read from Silhouette, and we've kept these comments and suggestions in mind in developing SILHOUETTE DESIRE.

DESIREs feature all of the elements you like to see in a romance, plus a more sensual, provocative story. So if you want to experience all the excitement, passion and joy of falling in love, then SILHOUETTE DESIRE is for you.

I hope you enjoy this book and all the wonderful stories to come from SILHOUETTE DESIRE. I'd appreciate any thoughts you'd like to share with us on new SILHOUETTE DESIRE, and I invite you to write to us at the address below:

Karen Solem
Editor-in-Chief
Silhouette Books
P.O. Box 769
New York, N.Y. 10019

STEPHANIE JAMES
Body
Guard

Silhouette Desire
Published by Silhouette Books New York

America's Publisher of Contemporary Romance

SILHOUETTE BOOKS, a Division of Simon & Schuster, Inc.
1230 Avenue of the Americas, New York, N.Y. 10020

Copyright © 1983 by Jayne Krentz, Inc.

Distributed by Pocket Books

ISBN: 0-671-45992-9

First Silhouette Books printing December, 1983

10 9 8 7 6 5 4 3 2 1

America's Publisher of Contemporary Romance

Printed in the U.S.A.

BC91

Other Silhouette Books by Stephanie James

For Sue and Keith and everyone at THE BOOKWORM in Richland, Washington. You'll never know how much all your kind words and encouragement have meant. Which means, I suppose, that some of these books are really all your fault!

1

Jake Devlin didn't look at all like a professional body-guard.

Sabrina McAllaster frowned down at the hastily scrawled address on the back of an old catalog card which she was holding in her left hand. No, the name and the street number were correct. She was at the right location.

The mildly annoyed frown continued to draw her soft, tawny brows together over clear hazel eyes as she stood in the doorway, peering into the large room. The floor of the room was covered with exercise mats, and in the center, sitting cross-legged, was the man who had just been pointed out as Jake Devlin.

In front of him, seated in two strict rows, were a dozen children six or seven years old. Each was dressed in a loose little outfit of white which resembled the clothing worn by people who took judo classes. But this wasn't a judo class. According to the small hand-lettered sign on the front door, Jake Devlin taught some exotic form of self-defense, the name of which was unfamiliar to Sabrina. The fact that she had never heard of it made it exotic indeed. Sabrina had collected a tremendous amount of trivial but fascinating information over the years. It was one of the more interesting aspects of her job as a college librarian.

"Isn't it incredible?" whispered one of the waiting mothers who occupied the small anteroom in which Sabrina was standing. "This is the only time during the entire week when Blake sits still for more than five seconds. I wish I knew that man's secret!"

Sabrina turned to smile questioningly at the attractive young woman behind her. "The kids do seem rather attentive," she murmured.

"That's putting it mildly! They love him. Hang on his every word. And the amazing part is that they actually seem to understand some of what he tells them. I can see how a kid that age would enjoy some of the exercises, but the fact that they seem to pay just as much attention to the philosophical part of the class amazes me!" The woman chuckled softly. "Believe me, I'm not complaining. I just wish Blake paid as much attention to me or his teacher!"

"What's he teaching them during this part of the class?" Sabrina asked curiously, her eyes sliding back to the scene in the large room. She couldn't hear what Devlin was saying to the children, although she caught the low, somewhat gritty masculine tones clearly. She found herself straining to listen.

The woman beside her shrugged ruefully. "I'm not sure. Whenever I ask Blake, he just tells me Mr. Devlin is teaching them to be 'strong.' Not just in their bodies but in their minds. I'm not sure Blake knows how to explain what he's learning in there, but whatever it is, it's good for him."

"Aren't you afraid he'll run out and beat up all the other little kids in his class?" Sabrina inquired dryly.

Blake's mother shook her head. "There's no doubt my son is learning to take care of himself at an incredibly early age, but he seems to be learning a respect for his own abilities at the same time." She grinned and held up crossed fingers. "So far, at least, I haven't had any angry calls from his teacher or from riled parents of fellow classmates!"

Another amused voice broke in on the discussion. "I have a daughter in this class and a son in one of the groups for older kids, and so far there's been no problem. My son tells me he knows he could handle any of the kids in his class, and because he knows it, he doesn't have to prove it."

Sabrina glanced at the pleasantly rounded redhead who had spoken. The anteroom was full of waiting mothers, all looking both proud and amazed at the progress their children were making. "I didn't realize Mr. Devlin taught classes for children," Sabrina noted weakly. Something about seeing a man surrounded by a dozen youngsters severely altered the image she'd formed in her head of a macho bodyguard.

"Kids are all he does teach," put in a third parent wisely. "He doesn't offer any classes for adults."

"Being surrounded by the little beasts all day long would drive me out of my skull," observed the first woman, her eyes moving ruefully back to the quiet scene in the exercise room. "Unless, of course, I had his magic trick of keeping them all so beautifully disciplined."

"The remarkable part is that he never even has to raise his voice," groaned someone. "I've been bringing Jonathan here now for three months, and not once have I ever seen Devlin shout at the kids or slap one on the behind. It's always like this. Perfect discipline."

Several mothers shook their heads in awe of the alien talent. Sabrina narrowed her gaze thoughtfully. "Perhaps they're scared to death of him?" she suggested.

That brought a laugh. "Not a chance. Wait and see what happens when the class is over."

At that moment Devlin clapped his hands once, sharply, and immediately all twelve children surged to their feet. Their instructor rose at the same time. Sabrina watched in fascination as the kids bowed gravely to Devlin and their equally grave teacher bowed in return.

Then, as if that were the signal, everything exploded back to normal. Sabrina found herself half-smiling as the twelve little students became twelve rowdy, excited children who had just been dismissed from class. Several came racing toward their waiting mothers, but a few continued to hang around Devlin as he started toward the doorway. With casual affection he ruffled the hair of a little boy who was eagerly telling him about a new frog he had at home. When another youngster trustingly grabbed for the man's hand, Devlin gave it to him. The twelve small martial-arts students circled and danced and skipped around the quiet man who walked in their midst.

Devlin wasn't wearing a white uniform as the children did. He had on a pair of faded denims and a black long-sleeved cotton knit shirt with a band collar. The body-hugging fabric of the shirt fit over a lean, smoothly muscled torso that had the supple, wiry look of a hunting cat. It was not the body of a weight lifter or a man who deliberately worked at building muscles. Like that of the cat, it was sinewy and radiated a sense of contained strength. The denims rode low on a flat waist and narrow hips, fitting closely to the sleek contours of his thighs. He was barefoot. She guessed his age as a hard thirty-five.

Sabrina eyed the man she had reluctantly come to hire. She wasn't absolutely certain what bodyguards were supposed to look like, but she had been expecting to find a gun-packing muscle-bound creature who probably wouldn't appear overly bright. And although she was rather relieved not to have to deal with such a person, Sabrina suddenly wasn't sure if what she had found was much of an improvement. After all, annoying as it might have been to deal with someone who resembled her mental image of a bodyguard, at least she would have known what she was getting into. A simple muscle-bound male with a gun might not be very pleasant to have around but he would probably be relatively easy to handle. Jake Devlin, Sabrina decided morosely, looked as if he were going to be anything but easy.

To begin with, there were those eyes. The cool gray gaze fixed on her at that moment as if he sensed her particular interest, and she found herself looking into unfathomable rain-colored depths. No, the man was definitely not simple.

Intelligent, aware and potentially deadly were the first adjectives that sprang into her head. Good Lord! What had she gotten herself into? Or, more accurately, what had her mother gotten her into?

The gray gaze flicked over her, assessing, summarizing, registering, and then it slid away to concentrate on the upturned face of a small sandy-haired boy who was earnestly yanking at the pocket of Devlin's jeans. It was like watching a bold, utterly heedless kitten trying to grab the attention of a lion, Sabrina thought wonderingly.

But then Jake Devlin glanced down at the boy and at once everything changed. Sabrina blinked in astonishment. It was as if the gray in those eyes turned from the cool, body-chilling rain of the dead of winter to the warm, gentle mists of summer. The line of Devlin's mouth, almost grim in repose, crooked upward in a half-smile that displayed a surprising indulgence. The softening touches could not completely obliterate the overall impact of what was basically not a handsome face, but somehow Sabrina found herself wanting to ignore the harsh, dark side of this man. Like the children, she wanted to respond to the hint of warmth.

As he looked down at the eager child, the overhead light gleamed for a moment on the closely trimmed darkness of Devlin's hair, revealing a subtle variegation in color. At first glance it had appeared almost black, but now Sabrina realized it was really a very intense shade of brown.

When he lifted his head again to chat with the waiting mothers, the touch of warmth disappeared as quickly as it had come. It was replaced by a cool, remote and very, very polite expression which encouraged nothing more than superficial friendliness. Suddenly Sabrina realized why none of the women had commented earlier on the man himself, only on his ability with their children. She knew at once that none of the cheerful mothers had ever gotten any closer to Jake Devlin than discussions on the progress of their offspring.

In that moment Sabrina would have been willing to bet that there were very few people on the face of the earth who could claim to be more than casually acquainted with Jake Devlin. Unfortunately her mother had apparently run into one of those few people.

It wasn't until the last of the enthusiastic children had departed with his mother that Jake quietly closed the door and turned to face his visitor.

"There don't appear to be any leftover kids hanging around," he noted in that low, slightly rough voice. For some reason that voice caught her attention, reverberating subtly along her nerve endings in a way that made Sabrina's cool frown deepen. "So I assume you're here to see me?"

"I'm Sabrina McAllaster, Mr. Devlin," she began crisply, extending her hand in what she hoped was a businesslike manner. "I believe you were told to expect a visit from me?"

He nodded once, a short, economical movement, and accepted the proffered fingers. Instantly Sabrina regretted having made the polite overture. As Devlin's hand surrounded her own much smaller one, something happened to the sense of feeling in the tips of her fingers. She lost it. Her whole hand tingled a little and then went numb!

You could tell a lot about a man by his handshake, her mother always claimed. Well, thought Sabrina as she hastily retrieved her assaulted fingers, if that was true, she had to conclude that Jake Devlin had no qualms about impressing a potential client with his particular art form. What had he done to her hand?

"I wasn't asking for a demonstration of your ability, Mr. Devlin," she gritted, moving her fingers experimentally to see if all were still functioning.

He appeared mildly surprised at her reaction to his handshake. "I wasn't providing a demonstration, Miss McAllaster. I was merely trying to do the polite thing. Did I hurt you?" he added with innocent concern.

"Don't worry about it," she managed wryly. "I'll soak it in Epsom salts when I get home."

"You're angry."

"Let's just say I don't appreciate heavy-handed men! And don't tell me you don't know what you did to my fingers!" she said tartly. "Because I saw you working out with those little kids. None of them seemed to be in any

13

danger and they're a lot smaller than I am!" She sank down onto a ragged chair near the worn-looking metal desk at the far end of the room.

"The kids like me," he explained gently, taking the frayed swivel chair behind the desk and leaning forward to rest his arms on top of the blotter. "I got the distinct impression that you don't."

She stared at him for an instant, startled by the comment. What had he seen in her to give him that idea? She wasn't conscious of not liking him, but Sabrina couldn't deny that her reaction to the man had been strong and immediate. She felt wary, a little uneasy, and sensed a need to remain totally in control of any situation involving him. None of those reactions was strange under the circumstances. But she didn't actively dislike him. "I'm sorry you got the feeling that I don't idolize you the way the children seem to do, but you must remember that this is my first experience with a professional body-guard. You'll have to forgive me if I'm not up on all the etiquette for dealing with one. Perhaps it would be best if we got on with the business end of this discussion, Mr. Devlin. I'm in something of a hurry."

"I'm sorry if I really hurt you," he murmured, glancing interestedly at her hand as it rested idly on her stylish black leather drawstring pouch.

"Are you?" she demanded skeptically. Actually the hand felt fine now and she suspected he knew it. He was the kind of man who would know exactly how much force he had used and how long the effects would last. Sabrina wasn't certain how she came to that conclusion but she was instinctively sure of her assessment. It only served to make her more wary and more irritated than ever with the whole situation.

"Yes," he replied with a sigh, sitting back in the chair, which squeaked under the imposition of the weight shift.

"I don't usually resort to that sort of childishness. But you did look awfully annoyed at finding yourself having to deal with me. I suppose for some perverse reason I wanted to show you how really annoying I can be. It won't happen again," he added crisply.

"Let's hope not," Sabrina muttered dryly, suddenly aware that he was mildly irked with himself for having succumbed to the small temptation to retaliate physically for her apparent slight. "Now, if you don't mind, I think it's time we talked business."

The unfathomable gray eyes moved over her once more. Sabrina had the feeling he'd seen everything he'd needed to see during the hard, quick perusal he'd given her as he walked off the exercise floor earlier. But now he appeared to want to take his time.

Impatiently she endured the absorbing glance, knowing exactly what he was seeing. Sabrina had no illusions about her looks. She was no beauty. Passably attractive was how she described herself when she was in a charitable mood. Not striking or beautiful, but passably attractive. As far as she was concerned, it was easier to list her faults than her good points.

Chief among those faults was that of being too short and too small all over. At five feet, two inches she was forced to buy most of her clothes in the petite sections of department stores, hem every pair of jeans she'd ever owned and look up to every man she'd ever dated, including the one she'd made the mistake of marrying. Over the years Sabrina had more than once wished for a little more height and a lot more physical strength.

The smallness extended to the gentle curves of her breasts, and buying size thirty-two-A bras was not one of Sabrina's favorite pastimes. Very often she simply didn't bother wearing a bra at all. The rest of her figure was in similar proportion. A tiny waist was set off by softly flared hips and thighs that filled out the rather dashing black denim jeans she was wearing. There was nothing skinny about Sabrina in spite of her stature.

The jeans were tight and had very narrow legs. She wore them with a pair of short soft leather boots, a long-sleeved white blouse and a buttery, close-fitting little black suede vest. The outfit made Sabrina feel a bit rakish and had given her the sense of bravado she needed to go calling on a professional bodyguard.

But the hard edge she had wanted to achieve with the slick, racy clothing was curiously at odds with the soft mass of her tawny brown hair, which was refusing to stay within the confines of the clip at the back of her head. Tendrils were already trailing down and the once-tight knot was becoming loose and slightly off-center.

The coiled hair was drawn back from a small, neat face. Wide hazel eyes dominated and, with their faintly tilted corners, added an elfin touch. Her small nose was sharply etched and her expressive mouth could smile easily or curve downward in a quick scowl. It was an interesting, mobile face, full of intelligence and lively animation, if not beauty, and in that respect it accurately reflected the woman behind it.

Sabrina had turned twenty-eight six months earlier, and her life-style—up until this farce of a situation which was forcing her to hire a bodyguard—was finally firmly under her control. That included the men in her life as well as her career and her quicksilver intellectual enthusiasms. Actually, the latter two had always been under control. It was her love life which had proved so hard to handle. Grimly Sabrina put that thought out of her mind. She was a different woman these days, no longer vulnerable and stupid where men were concerned.

"Well?" she demanded waspishly. "Will I do as a client?"

The gray gaze narrowed. "To tell you the truth, I'm not inclined to be overly choosy at the moment. I need the money."

"And I, unfortunately, can't afford to be overly choosy either," she tossed back, incensed. "I'm in a hurry. I don't have time to run all over Portland trying to find someone who will satisfy my mother."

"We seem to be stuck with each other." But there was a trace of humor in the statement and she thought she detected a faint softening in his controlled expression. "You're going to tolerate me just to please your mother?"

Sabrina winced, mouth twisting wryly. "I'm doing it to give her peace of mind, yes. She's so wrapped up in her work, so determined to get that military project finished on time for her company, that I don't want her having to worry about me on top of all the other things she has to worry about! Did that Mr. Teague person who's protecting her tell you the details?"

"He said the company your mother works for down in Los Angeles got the threats against its top executives on the project last week and, after consultation with Teague's agency, decided to take them seriously. They've provided all the high-profile executives like your mother with round-the-clock protection until the military contract is finished and the work can be turned over to the contracting agency."

"But Mom's firm isn't extending the protection to adult family members no longer living at home. Some of the other executives have decided to play cautious and have privately hired protection for their older sons and daughters who might be vulnerable. My mother apparently decided to do the same, although I can't for the life of me think why," Sabrina muttered, frowning again as she considered the huge monkey wrench which had been thrown into her plans.

"It doesn't seem so illogical to me," Jake Devlin observed mildly. "Teague said the threats looked pretty damn professional to him. The people making them want to make an example out of your mother's firm. They want that project halted with the maximum amount of publicity."

"It's ridiculous. Big business and the U.S. government don't halt important projects just because of a few threats!"

"No, but if these people decide to go all the way to achieve nationwide attention, there's no telling who could get hurt in the process."

"Well, I'm going to be in Hawaii tomorrow! Thousands of miles away from the West Coast and presumably thousands of miles away from potential lunatics," Sabrina said. "Protecting me is a waste of everyone's time and money."

Jake cocked an eyebrow. "You'll pardon me, I'm sure, if I say that I, for one, don't consider it exactly a waste of money." He ran a familiar eye around the somewhat shabby interior of his office-cum-waiting-room. "There's a lot I want to do with this place. I need a little capital to work with and, frankly, your mother is paying top dollar. Since the school is closed now for a couple of weeks anyway, the timing of this little side job couldn't have been better."

"I'm so glad someone is pleased with the situation!"

"You really are a bit upset about this, aren't you?" he noted with infuriating blandness. "Going to put a crimp in your plans?"

"It's not exactly going to add a light touch to my vacation, is it? Having an armed guard trailing around after me?" she grumbled.

He held up both of his hands, palms outward. "Look,

ma'am, no guns. I'll try not to appear like the heavy from a gangster film."

"Or from a kung-fu epic?" A dash of amusement flared in her eyes as she contemplated the ludicrousness of the situation in which she found herself.

"With any luck there will be no trail of dead bodies behind us to mark our passing. I'm nothing if not neat."

She thought about that for a moment, her head tipped to one side as she absently nibbled on her lower lip. She wasn't quite sure what to say next. How did one go about interviewing a bodyguard? Especially when one didn't have much choice? "I'm glad you're neat. Are you any good?"

"Since you're not expecting trouble, does it matter whether or not I'm any good?" he countered coolly.

"My mother likes to get what she pays for," Sabrina shot back firmly. "Why did this Teague person recommend you? How do you happen to know him?"

"I met Teague a long time ago. He knew I was living here in Portland, and when your mother asked him for a recommendation, he very kindly thought of me."

"That doesn't tell me a whole lot." It was all a little too pat, in fact, Sabrina decided silently. She knew almost nothing about this man, and here she was about to go off on a ten-day trip to Hawaii in his company!

"I'm sorry, I don't have an annotated biography of myself prepared to hand out to my clients, Miss Mc-Allaster. I'm afraid you'll just have to take me on trust and Teague's recommendation."

Sabrina absorbed the full impact of the quiet challenge he was issuing and then decided it was time to make a few points very clear. If they were going to be stuck with each other for the next couple of weeks, Jake Devlin had better learn who was in charge.

"I don't have to take you at all, Mr. Devlin. I can leave you behind when I board that plane for Hawaii tomorrow morning. With a bit of scrounging, in fact, I might be able to find someone else in Portland who would be willing to take on the assignment *and* prepare an annotated biography of himself!"

He appeared totally unmoved by that possibility. "It's too late. Teague had your mother wire me an advance of two weeks' salary. It arrived in my account this morning. I'm to begin my duties at six o'clock this evening, right after I close the school for the day."

"You're very sure of yourself," she drawled.

"When I accepted the position over the phone, Teague implied that the contract was signed and sealed. Your mother was apparently satisfied on her end," Jake murmured.

"My mother isn't the one who has to have you prowling about for the next two weeks! You never did answer my question," Sabrina said grimly. "Are you any good?"

"You mean will I take a bullet meant for you if it comes to that?"

Shocked at the suggestion, Sabrina sat back in her seat abruptly. Horror and disgust at the very notion of someone doing such a thing on her behalf were clearly visible on her expressive face. Eyes wide, she stared at him. "Absolutely not! That's the last thing in the world I'd want anyone to do! What a ghastly idea!"

"You wouldn't consider it a service for which your mother is paying?" he asked politely.

"Don't be ridiculous!"

"What, exactly, do you expect from a bodyguard, Miss McAllaster?"

She shrugged helplessly, feeling impatient and decidedly at a loss. "I don't know. I suppose you'll sort of keep an eye out for suspicious people or something."

"To a bodyguard, everyone looks suspicious."

"Then you'll be quite busy keeping an eye on folks, won't you? Look, Mr. Devlin, this is getting us nowhere. I haven't the least notion of how to interview you, and even if I did, it would probably be a waste of time. This Teague character has convinced my mother that you're entirely suitable for the job, so I guess I'll have to accept that for the time being." She got reluctantly to her feet and he immediately stood up and padded, barefoot, around the small desk.

"I appreciate your unlimited faith in my abilities." He half-smiled, following her as she made firmly for the front door. "I will do my best to live up to your expectations."

"Vague though those expectations may be?" she concluded for him, turning around to face him at the door. "But then, you're rather vague yourself, aren't you, Mr. Devlin? Have you done this sort of thing very much?"

"Guarded bodies? Nope." He appeared unconcerned by his lack of experience in the field. "I prefer teaching self-defense to little kids."

"I see," she responded stiffly. "But bodyguarding pays better?"

"Much better."

"And you need the money," she finished. "We do, indeed, appear to be stuck with each other, don't we, Mr. Devlin?" she added morosely.

"Try not to let it get you down. I'm sure Hawaii will be wonderful, even with me along. And you might as well call me Jake, since we're going to become such close acquaintances."

Sabrina eyed his polite expression mistrustfully, remembering what she had decided earlier about this man's probable lack of close acquaintances. "All right, Jake," she agreed slowly. Then she remembered something. "I suppose I ought to call the hotel in Hawaii and get another room for you."

"Teague arranged everything from his end," Jake said smoothly.

"An efficient sort, your Mr. Teague. Well, I'll, uh, see you around, I guess," Sabrina said a little weakly, not knowing exactly how one organized a bodyguard.

"Yes, you will," he agreed. "Around six o'clock this evening, to be exact."

Sabrina looked up at him blankly, uncomfortably aware of the strength and quiet power in him. From her perspective most men were a little too tall, a bit overwhelming physically, but there was something even more alarming about this man. One could find oneself having to strain one's neck looking up to a man without experiencing the concomitant fear of being somehow mentally or emotionally dominated by him. But this Jake Devlin made her uneasy in a way she couldn't quite describe. She told herself to be grateful that at least he wasn't a huge man. Jake Devlin probably stood a couple of inches under six feet. But that was more than tall enough as far as she was concerned.

"Six o'clock?" she repeated. "You want to see me at six?"

"That's when my job is scheduled to begin, remember?" he reminded her gently.

"Oh. You needn't bother starting quite that soon," she assured him blithely. "I'll meet you at the airport tomorrow morning. That should be soon enough to begin this bodyguarding business. Don't forget your swimsuit, by the way. Since you won't have much to do in Hawaii, it will be a great opportunity to do a little skin diving or something. You can swim, can't you?'' she added with quick concern.

"I get by. Sabrina, you don't seem to understand how this is going to work," Jake began carefully, as if seeking the words with which to explain his role. "I'm supposed to look after you on a round-the-clock basis and I'm supposed to start after I conduct my last class of the day today."

"Don't worry." She smiled, realizing what was troubling him. "I won't tell your Mr. Teague that we delayed the actual start of the job until tomorrow. You'll get to keep your full two weeks' salary."

He just looked at her as if she weren't particularly bright. "Six o'clock tonight. I have your address." He emphasized each word.

Sabrina allowed her simmering annoyance to become a full-scale boil as she acknowledged that she might be dealing with an extremely literal-minded male. "Jake, I'm going to be busy tonight," she stated bluntly. "I won't be in until quite late. If you like, I can promise to call when I do get in and let you know that I'm safe and sound, but that's all I can promise. I will be with other people this evening, friends, so there's no need for you to worry about me. I think it would be a good idea if we got something quite clear between us. You will be working for me, not the other way around. Within limits I will try to cooperate with your security measures, but I will not have my whole life turned upside down by this perfectly ridiculous fear of my mother's."

She pulled open the outer door of the office with a brisk gesture and stepped out into the hall. Flinging the leather straps of her small bag over one shoulder, she confronted him. Booted feet braced slightly apart, her small fists on her hips and a severe frown knitting her brows, Sabrina appeared a little like a tiny Robin Hood dressed in black and white. All she lacked was the bow and a hat with a feather. Devlin simply stared at her as if at some alien being.

"I assume," she continued deliberately, "that the famous Mr. Teague has also taken care of your airline ticket."

"He has."

"Then there's really no need for us to see each other again until tomorrow morning. I'm sorry we've gotten off on a somewhat awkward footing, Jake," she went on, relenting a bit as she told herself that this wasn't really his fault. "But perhaps it's just as well that everything's clear between us. I'm not going to allow this bodyguarding business to ruin my vacation. I don't believe for one moment that I'm in any genuine danger, so there's no need to work too hard at your job. I'm sure if we both try we can get through the next couple of weeks on a reasonably amicable basis. The key to that, however, will be for you to remember that you take your orders from me."

"You're making your position quite clear," he drawled a little too softly.

Sabrina chose to ignore the faint warning which nibbled at her nerves. "Good. Then I see no reason why we shouldn't be able to get along. I shall be quite busy while we're in Hawaii. I'm combining my vacation with a seminar being held at the hotel. That will leave you plenty of free time to enjoy your trip. Neither of us should suffer unduly if we just stay out of each other's way."

"You don't see any contradiction in the idea of my trying to guard you while staying out of your way?" he goaded gently.

"I'm sure we'll work something out. We'll discuss the details on the plane. It's a long trip." Whirling on one heel, Sabrina strode firmly down the corridor with all the dignity she could command.

Once outside the building, she dug her keys out of the black bag and stalked toward the small MG which waited at the curb. The interview had not gone at all well and at least part of the fault lay with herself. She was honest enough to admit that much. Gritting her teeth in silent exasperation, she slid into the little bucket seat and started the engine with a swift twist of the key.

Damn! What a mess. Well, she would do what she could to smooth things over during the long flight to Hawaii. If she didn't, the next two weeks might be among the longest of her life. She had been so looking forward to the upcoming trip. It would be most aggravating if she failed to enjoy it because of the presence of her new bodyguard.

Having a bodyguard was undoubtedly much simpler for her busy, efficient mother. Mrs. McAllaster, Sabrina knew, was practically living full-time at the office during these last few hectic days of the project. The man assigned to protect her probably just stood unobtrusively outside her office door during the sixteen-hour days she was putting in and then followed her home at night and checked the electronic gear which had been installed around the apartment.

But for Sabrina it was a lot more complicated. A vacation routine was, by nature, eclectic, to say the least. She certainly didn't intend to confine herself unnecessarily, especially since she was sure the whole thing was entirely uncalled for. Big companies were always subject to numerous threats from various and assorted nuts. It was becoming a sign of prestige, in fact, for an executive to receive personal protection from his or her firm. It marked a certain level of importance in the corporate world, like having a key to the executive washroom.

Still, her mother's peace of mind was important to Sabrina. The affection between mother and daughter was very real, even though Sabrina had gone her own way in life. Sabrina had a tremendous amount of respect for the woman who had achieved such a high level of success in the business world after being abandoned by her husband when her daughter was only ten years old. That respect and love were sufficient reasons for Sabrina to go along with her mother's wishes in this matter.

But she would do so on her own terms, Sabrina vowed as she sent the little car leaping away from the curb with her usual abandon. She would have to impress that point on Jake Devlin.

Three stories above, the man in question stood gazing out the window as Sabrina maneuvered the bright red MG through traffic with what seemed an utter disregard for the rules of driving safety. She drove quite literally like a small bat out of hell, he decided, leaning forward to plant both palms on the windowsill. He got the feeling she did everything in life the way she drove her MG. With bright, enthusiastic energy and an irrepressible spirit.

Guarding such a creature was going to be like running after a butterfly with a net. On top of everything else, this was one butterfly who thought she could set down rules for the guy with the net.

Jake Devlin stood staring out the window at the Portland, Oregon, skyline for a long while after the red MG had disappeared. He had never tried to capture a butterfly in a net. But for his own peace of mind during the next couple of weeks, as well as for her personal safety, he'd better find a way to teach his new client that the poor guy with the net was a force with which to be reckoned.

It was going to be a long night, Jake reflected as he turned away from the window at last. But then, a lot of his nights were long. Much too long.

At least tonight he'd have a reason for being awake while the rest of the world slept. He had a job to do.

2

~~~~~~~~~~~~

Rick Shepherd was becoming a nuisance. Sabrina slanted her escort a cautious glance as he slipped one arm around her waist in a familiar fashion and guided her to a darkened end of the huge porch. The sounds of the party drifted out to the pair as they stood looking down the hillside at the sea of lights that was Portland. In the distance the multitude of bridges that crossed the busy Willamette River glittered like strings of necklaces. Sabrina's apartment building was close to one of those bridges and overlooked the river. It seemed a long way away tonight. Soon she would have to make some excuse and start the trip back down the mountain toward town. It was getting late.

"I'll miss you during the next ten days, honey," Rick murmured, the fingers of the hand at her waist making what he undoubtedly thought was a seductive movement. "I wish I could go with you."

"You'd be bored to tears spending ten days in seminars, and you know it, Rick," she scoffed lightly. He was a good-looking man, she told herself disinterestedly. That carefully tousled blond hair, those sexy bedroom eyes of deepest blue and that rugged profile would have had most women canceling the ten-day Hawaiian trip in a flash. Men like Rick weren't likely to be waiting around when a woman finally got back from a long trip.

But Sabrina no longer canceled plans on account of men, handsome or otherwise. She no longer allowed men to exercise anything more than a very casual influence over her life. It was so much safer that way.

"Do you always combine your vacations with some dull educational program?" Rick complained with mild disgust. He edged her more closely against his body, ignoring her faint resistance. "Didn't you tell me that during the Christmas break you signed up for a Caribbean cruise which was featuring classes on Shakespeare's plays?"

"A fabulous trip," Sabrina said enthusiastically, hazel eyes sparkling. "The people organizing the classes brought a company of actors on board and they did a different play every night. During the days we studied the piece that was due to be performed. I learned so much!"

"I can think of a hell of a lot of other things I'd rather do on a cruise than attend plays! And what about that three-day weekend last month when you disappeared down to California to go to a seminar on wine-tasting? I mean, I like wine, but to spend a whole three-day weekend having to study the stuff?"

"I can now rest assured that I will never disgrace myself in a restaurant again," she informed him with mock solemnity. Sabrina tried to edge away from the proximity of his body, and frowned in annoyance when he refused to loosen his hold. Yes, Rick was definitely becoming a nuisance. "Don't stockbrokers ever attend classes and self-improvement seminars?"

"Only the ones that are guaranteed to help us find new clients and promote sales! Do you know where I spent the Christmas holidays this year? Down in Mexico, lying on an Acapulco beach and sipping margaritas!"

"I expect I'll get in a few mai tais while I'm in Hawaii," she chuckled.

"If I were with you, we'd enjoy a lot more than that," he murmured, lowering his head to nuzzle her ear with a confidence that further annoyed Sabrina.

"But you're not going to be with me, are you, Rick? So what we might or might not enjoy together really doesn't matter. Now, if you'll excuse me, I think it's time I went home. I was going to start my packing tonight. I leave tomorrow morning, you know." Very firmly Sabrina made to step away from his encircling arm.

"Ah, Sabrina, what's the matter with you? I thought we could go back to my place this evening when we left here." The trace of petulance in his voice and the way his arm tightened in response to her efforts to free herself brought a glowing spark of impatience to Sabrina's eyes.

"Some other time, Rick. I told you I wouldn't be able to stay late tonight. That's why I insisted on driving myself to the party. Please excuse me, I'm going to leave."

She snapped around abruptly, successfully breaking his grip on her waist with the quickness of her movement, and strode briskly back toward the French doors which led into the crowded living room. Her small figure, as lithe and confident as a matador's, was clad in turquoise velvet gaucho pants, silver-studded bolero jacket and gold lamé blouse. Her feet, in black slippers with silver heels, tapped out an impatient, annoyed beat as she crossed the wooden boards of the porch. Her tawny hair, once again in a twist at the back of her head, caught the light just as she slipped through the doors. She could feel Rick's brooding gaze on her as she walked away from him, and was glad of the cheerful, noisy crowd waiting in the living room.

The trip to Hawaii was occurring at a very convenient time. It would serve nicely to sever the relationship with Rick Shepherd, she decided as she smilingly took her leave of her hostess. Rick had begun pushing for a much more intimate association than Sabrina was willing to allow any man these days. Emotional safety, she had learned the hard way, lay in being the one in control of a relationship. It lay in never allowing a man to know you were vulnerable to him. Men did not respect or cherish vulnerability, Sabrina knew. They took advantage of it.

"I'm sorry you have to go so soon," Maggie Compton said regretfully as Sabrina thanked her for the invitation. "I hope you have a wonderful time in Hawaii. What is it this time? A class on tropical flowers?" she added with a knowing chuckle.

"Arthurian legends and the Age of Chivalry." Sabrina grinned back. "You should see the stack of books I had to buy. They take up one full suitcase!"

"Well, don't spend all your time reading on the beach," Maggie instructed firmly. "This is supposed to be a vacation!"

"Oh, it will be. The kind of vacation I like best."

The older woman shook her head. "You and your classes and projects! I can hardly keep track of what you're into from one week to the next. Don't forget to take a look around at the rest of your classmates. Maybe you'll find a genuine knight in shining armor. What better place to discover one than in a class on chivalry?"

Sabrina's mouth curved wryly. "Maggie, knights in

shining armor are as rare as unicorns these days, and you know it. But I promise to bring back a full report of the lectures if you really want it."

"Spare me! Unlike you, my interests don't run the gamut from wine-tasting to Arthurian legends and every odd byway in the middle. What on earth do you do with all the miscellaneous facts and trivia you learn at all these seminars, Sabrina?"

"A librarian can use all sorts of tidbits in her work. Besides, look at the wealth of conversational material it gives me for chatting with strangers at parties like this one! Good night, Maggie. I'll send you a postcard from Hawaii!"

With a casual wave, Sabrina took her leave, escaping through the front door of the elegant hillside home. The party had been a pleasant one as parties went, and Maggie Compton was a good friend, but Sabrina had had enough for one evening. And she really did have to start packing for her trip. She realized as she hurried down the steps toward the row of cars parked along the winding street that she wasn't even particularly curious about whom Rick Shepherd might take home later that night. She nodded her head once in silent satisfaction. She'd come a long way since that fateful decision two years ago when she had made up her mind once and for all to treat men the same way she treated her various and assorted intellectual interests. Like the many classes and seminars she attended, her current relationships tended to be short-lived, amusing and emotionally uninvolving.

And life, Sabrina assured herself as she dug out the keys to the MG, had never been better. She had just about everything she wanted, didn't she? Not including this bodyguard she was stuck with, naturally. Oh, well. If it made her busy mother happier to know her daughter was going to Hawaii accompanied by someone out of a kung-fu film, she, Sabrina, could tolerate it. The vague threats which had come into the headquarters of her mother's high-technology firm would soon be dealt with, she was certain. For ten days she could put up with the inconvenience of a baby-sitter. Perhaps he could busy himself teaching self-defense to little kids on the beach.

That thought made her smile whimsically. How many professional bodyguards taught children as a source of regular income? She was still smiling faintly when she reached the MG and bent down to unlock the door.

Sabrina never even heard the shadowy figure which materialized out of the darkness behind her. The instinctive scream which came to her lips as she felt the touch of a man's hand was silenced before it began, cut off by the hard, callused palm which clamped itself over her mouth.

In her panic Sabrina kicked out wildly, struggling with the ferocity of a small cornered animal fighting for its life. But her captor overwhelmed her with frightening ease. He didn't strike her, yet she was rendered helpless in a matter of seconds, her wrists bound behind her with a strip of cloth, her mouth and eyes sealed with more of the same. The attacker said nothing during the entire process of binding her, not wasting breath on useless warnings against struggling. Sabrina got the impression he didn't particularly care whether or not she fought back. The end result would be the same.

Within seconds she was being swept off her feet and dumped into the passenger seat of the MG. Trembling with a rage which bordered on fear, she tried to throw herself back out of the car and onto the sidewalk. How could this be happening right here in front of Maggie Compton's home? Surely one of the other guests would emerge in a moment and give the alarm? Things like this just couldn't take place to people like her!

Her attempt to wriggle out of the car was halted when

the door was securely locked. Trapped in her blindness, unable to move her hands or feet, Sabrina could only sit huddled in the seat, waiting for whatever came next. There was no sense in struggling now. She was helpless for the moment. All she could do was conserve her energy and pray for an opportunity to escape.

What was her attacker doing, throwing her into her own car?

In an instant she had her answer. She sensed the masculine body sliding into the driver's seat, heard the key as it was inserted in the ignition, and then the MG was moving almost sedately away from the curb. Sedately, she thought hysterically. She had been kidnapped by a man who could move with terrible efficiency, a blinding swiftness that rendered his victim defenseless in seconds. Yet he drove her sporty little car as if it were a placid station wagon.

Stop it, she ordered herself silently. *This is no time for hysteria. My God! Mother was right to worry.* That man she had gone to see today, Jake Devlin, he had been right, too. For heaven's sake. Where was a bodyguard when you needed one? Chilled and shocked, Sabrina sat very still in the bucket seat. She had to think, had to keep her senses from succumbing completely to the fear which threatened to envelop her.

The MG made its way down the twisting road which led out of the hills and back into the main downtown area. Under the guidance of its new driver the spirited car made the trip down in a far less enthusiastic fashion than it had climbed up earlier. Carefully, sedately, with due regard to anyone else who might be on the road, the MG descended.

Sabrina was mentally trying to keep her bearings, waiting for the feeling of descent to slacken. As soon as they were down out of the hills, she would have a tough

34

time discerning which direction they were headed. But a great deal could depend on her ability to keep some sense of direction, she reminded herself frantically. Then, before they had reached the bottom of the hillside, the MG slowed and was brought gently to a halt beside the road.

Sabrina's breath refused to move out of her chest. There was no reason to come to a halt here unless . . . She swallowed heavily, her pulse pounding with fear-induced adrenaline. Unless whoever was driving had decided to dispose of an unwanted passenger.

No, that couldn't be the case. She was no good to anyone dead, surely? But the lunatic fringe which had sent the threatening notes to her mother's firm was just that, Sabrina thought grimly. Lunatic. Her only chance would be to talk. She might be able to convince them she was of more use alive if she could just get the gag out of her mouth.

The MG came to a complete stop and the engine was switched off. Her body tight with fear, Sabrina waited for whatever came next.

She flinched as the strong, callused hand touched her head, and then the blindfold was pulled free. Sabrina's eyes flew open as she got her first look at her abductor.

"You see how very, very easy it would be, Sabrina?" Jake Devlin lounged back against the door on the driver's side, one arm lazily draped along the curve of the steering wheel. With his other hand he did something to the gag, and it too fell away. Sabrina's soft mouth was half-open in stunned amazement as she absorbed the implications of her kidnapper's identity.

"Devlin!" she managed in a hoarse whisper. *"Devlin!"* She made the name sound more like a curse, but that didn't seem to faze him. He sat shrouded in the darkness of the car, his hard face implacable and emotionless in the pale light of the moon. He was dressed as he had been earlier, in jeans and a dark knit shirt, except that, instead of being barefoot, he wore a pair of soft suede shoes that looked something like moccasins. Tonight he seemed a dangerous devil of a man, a natural part of the night around him. Sabrina had never known real fear before in her life, she discovered. It washed over her now, intermingling with rage.

"I'm sorry about the theatrics, Sabrina," Jake Devlin went on quietly, leaning forward to reach around behind her body and untie her wrists. "But I had the feeling an object lesson was in order."

"An object lesson," she repeated, dumbfounded. She gave her head a dazed shake. "You did this to teach me a lesson?" When her hands were freed, she edged as far away from him as possible. "A *lesson?*"

"You made it pretty damned obvious today that you weren't taking the threats seriously. I thought it might be helpful if you were made to realize that no one is invulnerable."

Sabrina tried to respond and found her lips were parched. Moistening them with the tip of her tongue, she drew in a deep breath and tried again. "You're not actually kidnapping me? This was all some sort of scheme to teach me a lesson?" Each word was uttered with great care. She wanted to be absolutely certain.

"I wanted you to see for yourself how very easy it would be for someone to find you, catch you and use you," he replied deliberately. "I wanted you to understand why Teague and your mother think you need a bodyguard."

Sabrina sucked in her breath again and said the first words that came into her head. "You're fired!"

Devlin stared at her for a second and then his mouth

crooked unwillingly into a semblance of a slow grin. "You can't fire me."

"Because you're going to quit?" she shot back, fiercely hopeful.

"No such luck. I told you, your mother's money is already in my bank account. I've accepted the job of looking after you, Sabrina, and I intend to do my best. I thought it might be easier on both of us if we got a few of the ground rules established tonight, however."

"I'm the client! I make the ground rules!" she hissed.

"I can't let you do that, not when your way leaves you vulnerable. Sabrina, I could have been anyone tonight, don't you see? It was easy to follow you to that party and even simpler to pick you up on the street when you left. Anyone else could have done the same thing I did. Hell, you didn't even take a good look around before you walked away from the house to get into your car. Why didn't you at least have someone walk you out to it?"

"Because I was tired of the particular someone I might have asked. Just as I'm getting tired of you," she tossed back too sweetly. "And if you think I'm taking you with me to Hawaii after this ridiculous stunt, you've taken one too many falls during your martial-arts practice!"

Jake said nothing, shifting in the seat to switch the car's engine back on. Without a word he pulled away from the shoulder and started the MG back toward the city.

"I mean it, Jake Devlin," Sabrina lashed out furiously. "If you think—"

"We'll talk about it back at your apartment. It's getting late."

"There's nothing to talk about! If you won't accept the fact that I'm firing you, I'll call my mother and have her do it!"

"That's all your mother needs, isn't it? She's already

worried sick about your safety. If you were to leave for Hawaii without any protection, she'd really have something to concern her."

Sabrina bit back a sharp retort, knowing perfectly well that he was correct in his assessment of the situation. She was, after all, submitting to the notion of hiring a bodyguard purely for her mother's peace of mind. Firing the chosen nursemaid on the eve of the Hawaiian trip would not be a move calculated to set her mother's mind at ease. Sabrina closed her eyes briefly in disgust, feeling trapped.

"What you did tonight was absolutely uncalled for," she finally got out after a few minutes, staring straight ahead at the oncoming traffic.

"I needed to make you aware of how vulnerable you really are, Sabrina." There was no apology in the rough, gritty voice now.

"Just doing your job, is that it?" she muttered. It was ironic that he talked of her vulnerability. She had always thought of being vulnerable in the sense of taking an emotional risk. It was something she had painstakingly corrected after years of being far too unprotected, too honest and too hopeful of finding love, first from a father who had deserted her, then from a husband who had used her. Now, just as she had been congratulating herself on having built strong, secure walls around her emotions, she was confronted with a whole new kind of danger. This time it was a very real and physical danger. All the emotional barricades in the world couldn't protect her from crazy lunatics and kidnappers. Or, apparently, from the man assigned to protect her from such people.

"Who's going to protect me from my bodyguard?" she asked caustically when he refused to respond to her previous remark.

She sensed a tightening in him, a controlled violence

that made itself felt in the small confines of the car. "You have nothing to fear from me, Sabrina."

"After what just happened? That's a joke!"

"Nothing happened except that you got a hell of a scare. In another few minutes you'll be home, safe and sound in your own bed."

"What are you going to do? Stand watch in front of my door all night long?" she grumbled.

"Something like that." Was that a trace of humor underlying his words?

His response brought her sharply around in the seat. "Oh, no, Jake Devlin! Enough is enough. You're not going to spend the night marching up and down in the corridor outside my apartment. What would the neighbors think?" she demanded, appalled at the image.

He shot her a half-curious glance and then brought his gaze carefully back to the street in front of him. "Don't worry. I won't be standing guard in the corridor tonight."

"Then where will you be?" she snapped, not trusting him an inch now.

"How long is your couch?" he countered mildly.

"My couch! You think I'm going to let you sleep on my couch?" she blazed.

"Sabrina, I don't think you quite understand what having a bodyguard entails," he began carefully, as if to someone who was not overly bright. "I need to be within shouting distance of you all the time. That's what I'm being paid to do. For tonight that means bunking down in your living room or a spare bedroom if you've got one. Do you?"

"No, I do not!"

"Then that leaves me with the couch, doesn't it? Unless, of course, you want to take the couch and give me your bed?"

Sabrina, who had been half-expecting some provocative remark about *sharing* her bed with him, privately gave him credit for resisting the temptation to make such a crack. In spite of the fiasco this evening, she was beginning to get the feeling that her new bodyguard took his work seriously. Professionalism on any level was something she could respect. Up to a point.

"You're sure this is how it's done? Guarding someone, I mean," she asked suspiciously, peering across at his profile.

"It's how I'm going to do it," he answered with a negligent shrug.

Sabrina slouched down in her seat, folding her arms across her breasts and contemplating the city lights around her. "This," she announced finally, "could be the longest two weeks of my life."

She could feel him withdrawing, retreating behind a determinedly polite facade. "I'll try not to ruin the Hawaiian trip for you," Jake muttered softly.

For some crazy reason Sabrina almost felt like apologizing. Which was utterly ridiculous under the circumstances. "About what happened tonight . . ." she made herself say breezily.

"Yes?" he prompted cautiously, sliding a quick glance across at her.

"I'll get even, you know. Sooner or later, I'll get even for that stunt you pulled." She made it a throwaway line, a light remark which might have been taken as teasing or smiling bravado or a firm promise. She'd let him make of it what he would.

"Thank you for the warning," Jake drawled. "I'll be prepared."

But the real meaning behind the casual threat, of course, was that she was acquiescing to her plight. Sabrina recognized that fact for what it was and had a hunch Jake did the same. He had won. She didn't like the situation but she was intelligent enough to know that to go on fighting it was only going to lead to more scenes such as the embarrassing and frightening one which had just taken place outside Maggie Compton's home. Her one option was to get rid of Jake Devlin, and there simply wasn't any time, even if she could convince her mother that he was not the right bodyguard for her.

Her mother needed the next couple of weeks as worry-free as possible. That left Sabrina at the mercy of her new bodyguard.

"Got it all worked out?" Jake finally asked as he slowed the MG for the turn into the underground garage of Sabrina's apartment building. She didn't bother to ask how he knew her address. Teague would have given it to him. The mysterious Mr. Teague seemed quite efficient.

"You mean am I going to accept Teague's and my mother's choice in baby-sitters?" Sabrina didn't pretend not to know what he meant.

"Something like that. Which parking slot is yours?"

"Number thirty-four. Yes, I'm going to tolerate the situation for now. I don't have much choice, do I?"

"No." It was a simple statement, not intended to goad her further.

But its very matter-of-factness was more annoying than just about anything he could have said. Sabrina found herself deliberately biting her lip in order to keep from flinging back the sharp retort she felt he deserved. Something told her he would simply counter each new attack with whatever degree of effort it took to squelch it. Very professional, she thought with a groan as she slammed open the car door and jumped out.

The ride up to her apartment on the eleventh floor took place in utter silence. A brooding one on Sabrina's part; a seemingly unemotional one on Jake's. He politely took her key at the door and let them into her cheerfully decorated home. Without any apology he went in first and stood silently in the darkened interior for a long moment. Then he nodded calmly at Sabrina, who walked in obediently, lifting her eyes heavenward in supplication. Two weeks of this kind of thing? She was going to go crazy!

The apartment was furnished precisely to her taste. Sabrina no longer worried about pleasing anyone else these days. Peach and soft green and light beige provided the main tones of the color scheme, creating a light, fresh-air feel in the living room. A huge arrangement of brilliant long-stemmed gladioli occupied the center of the wide, low table in front of the peach-colored banquettes. The table was white and highly polished and, in addition to the flowers, was littered with a collection of books on King Arthur and medieval history.

The sight of the books reminded Sabrina of her plans for the rest of the evening. "I've got to finish packing," she stated, moving to collect the books. "What about you?"

Jake shrugged dismissingly. "I'll pick up my stuff on the way to the airport in the morning."

"Where's your car?"

"At my apartment. After I learned where the party was, I drove back home and I took a cab to your friend's house."

"I see." Sabrina glanced around uncertainly. "Well, make yourself comfortable, I guess," she said ungraciously. "I'm going to go pack."

For the next hour she did exactly that, tossing all the books into one suitcase and her clothes into another. As she bustled around the apartment, Jake seemed to ignore her, occupying himself by thumbing through one of her medieval texts. His concentration appeared total, she realized at one point. He didn't even glance up as she walked through the living room carrying a handful of lingerie she had just taken out of her small dryer. A very serious man, she thought with an inner sigh. Too bad Mr. Teague hadn't been able to come up with someone else in Portland, someone who had a more easygoing style and a sense of humor.

She didn't really feel particularly awkward with him in the apartment, however, and that was probably because of his serious, quiet way. There were no innuendos or veiled sexual jokes. His businesslike approach to the situation might, in the long run, be for the best, she acknowledged. Jake Devlin wasn't going to be a lot of fun to have around, but she wasn't going to have to fight him off, either.

"That's it for me," she finally announced, locking a suitcase and moving to stand in the bedroom doorway. "I'm going to bed. Turn out the lights, will you? Oh, and, uh, don't forget to lock the front door," she added with dry humor.

He looked up, his cool gaze colliding with hers. If he was aware of her mockery he gave no sign of it. "I'll try to remember. Good night, Sabrina, and . . ."

"Yes?" She tilted her head to one side inquiringly.

"And I'm sorry about tonight."

"Uh-huh. Just doing your job, weren't you?" Very firmly she closed her bedroom door.

The light from the hall fixture was switched off fifteen minutes later, just as Sabrina drifted off to sleep. She was vaguely aware of him rustling around in her living room, arranging the sheets and blankets she'd found for him, and then all was quiet.

But the shaft of light had reappeared under her door two hours later when Sabrina awoke with a start. For long moments she lay very quietly in bed, staring into the darkness and trying to pinpoint whatever it was that had awakened her. Was she nervous because she had a stranger in the house?

Then the light under the door caught her attention and she frowned as she slowly pushed back the covers and reached for her plush yellow robe. What was Jake doing up? He'd gone to bed at the same time she had. Good grief, she thought, glancing at the clock. It was nearly two in the morning and they had a long trip ahead of them the next day.

Knotting the sash of the robe, she padded barefoot to the door of her room and cautiously opened it. If Jake was up, she wanted to be careful about surprising him. Men like him probably slept in the nude!

With that thought in mind she called his name softly before emerging into the hall. "Jake?"

Soundlessly he appeared at the far end of the short hall, wearing his jeans, she was relieved to see. That was all he had on, however, and in the soft glow of the lamp behind him the skin of his shoulders appeared very sleek. The mat of dark, curling hair on his smoothly muscled chest tapered down to a point and disappeared beneath the waistband of the jeans. He, too, was barefoot and the pelt of hair on his head was tousled from the pillow.

For a startling, uncomfortable moment Sabrina felt as if she'd invited a dangerous and unpredictable male animal into her cozy apartment. Then he spoke, his voice deep and gentle, as if he sensed her unease. "It's all right, Sabrina. Go back to sleep. I'm sorry I woke you."

"Is anything wrong?"

"No, nothing's wrong."

"What are you doing up at this time of night?" she persisted, taking another step out into the hall. Her hair cascaded in disarray around her shoulders and her hazel eyes were half-slumberous, half-questioning. She stood blinking owlishly at him, waiting for some explanation.

44

"I'm not very sleepy," he muttered, moving back into the living room with a restlessness which surprised her. "Go back to bed, Sabrina."

"Why aren't you sleepy? Are you one of those people who only need a couple of hours a night or something? Is that part of being a good bodyguard?" She traipsed slowly down the hall, realizing that the sliding glass door onto the balcony was wide open. "Good Lord! It's freezing in here! Why on earth is the door open?"

"I wanted a little fresh air," he explained shortly, gliding across the room to shut the offending door with a quick, impatient motion. "Sorry."

Something caught her attention, something about the way he moved, the tone of his voice. "Are you all right, Jake?" she whispered.

His head snapped around and he shot her an unreadable glance. "I'm fine."

"Do you suffer from insomnia or anything?"

"No!" This time the denial was a small explosion of sound which he obviously regretted at once. "No, I don't suffer from insomnia," he went on deliberately.

"Well, thank God for that. It would drive me crazy having to put up with someone prowling around all night long for the next two weeks," she asserted calmly, making up her mind and heading for the kitchen. She knew all the signs and she knew the cure. "Nightmare, hmmm?"

"I beg your pardon?" Blankly he stared after her as she disappeared into the neat little kitchen and opened the refrigerator door. He came to stand behind her, leaning against the jamb. "What are you doing?"

"Fixing up the cure." She hauled the milk out and fumbled for a pan in the cupboard.

"Sabrina," he said slowly, beginning to comprehend, "I didn't have a nightmare. I was just a little restless. It

45

happens sometimes in strange surroundings," he added vaguely.

"It's all right, you don't have to be embarrassed. I'm an expert on nightmares." She poured the milk into the pan and began heating it, eyeing the warming liquid as she stifled a yawn with her free hand.

"You are?" He sounded confused.

"Yup. Used to suffer from them when I was about ten years old. Had a horrible time. Got to the point where I wouldn't even go to bed in an unlighted room. But Mom and I hit upon a cure." She switched off the stove and poured the milk into two mugs. "Come on. This is step one. Step two is television."

He moved aside in the doorway as she floated past, the yellow robe trailing out behind her like the train of a gown. Unable to do anything else, Jake followed her to one of the peach-colored banquettes, not the one on which he had been sleeping.

"First we find a late, late show on TV." Sabrina switched on the television and industriously began flipping channels until she found an old musical from the 1950's. "Ah, just what the doctor ordered. You'll be asleep in no time."

Flinging herself down on the banquette, she motioned for him to sit beside her. "Put your feet up on the table," she instructed, handing him a mug of hot milk, "and drink this."

"Sabrina, I . . ." He paused, unable to think of what to say. "It wasn't a nightmare that woke me up. I appreciate all this effort, but there's really no need to . . ."

She tugged him down beside her, careful not to spill the milk, and had a small shock when her fingers touched the sinewy length of his bare arm. But he came down obediently beside her and stretched out his bare feet alongside hers on the low white table. In front of them the

ridiculous musical blared forth cheerfully. Sabrina removed her copper-tinted nails from his arm swiftly,
unexpectedly aware of the feel of him, despite her
sleepiness.

"Now, you just slouch down against the pillows and sip
hot milk and stare at the tube. Works like magic."

"I see." For the first time he sounded somewhat
amused. Deliberately he took a sip of milk. "Yuck."

"Think of it as medicine."

"Is that how you thought of it when you were ten?" he
asked curiously.

"Yes. I've always hated milk but it does help in cases
like this. There's a special enzyme or something in it
which promotes sleep. I read about it somewhere," she
explained vaguely, tossing out one of her small bits of
trivia.

"Why did you have nightmares when you were ten?"
Jake inquired gently.

"I was going through a ten-year-old's emotional crisis," she tossed back flippantly.

"Unrequited love?" he asked, smiling.

"Something like that. My father deserted my mother
and me."

"Oh. I'm sorry, Sabrina, I didn't mean to make a joke
out of it," he apologized at once.

She relented, slanting him a sideways glance. "It's
okay. I'm quite recovered. Never got nightmares after I
turned eleven and fully accepted the situation."

He nodded and said nothing, sipping at his milk. For a
few minutes they sat watching the musical in an almost
companionable silence and then Sabrina felt her eyelids
growing heavy again. She yawned extravagantly. "Do
you think you'll be all right now?" she inquired politely.

"Yes, thank you. I'll be fine."

"Good. In another few minutes I'll go back to bed."

She should start back down the hall to her room right now, she told herself silently. But she felt oddly tempted to remain beside him awhile longer. He seemed pleasantly warm and unthreatening, in spite of that stupid stunt he'd pulled earlier. And now that she knew he had a very human sort of weakness, she thought it might be much easier to tolerate him for the next two weeks. Safe and unthreatening. Just the way she liked her men. Sabrina's lashes drooped and quite suddenly she was sound asleep.

Jake drank the last of his milk, making a wry face as he softly set the mug down on the table and turned to glance at his unwilling hostess. He removed the empty mug from her hand, setting it beside his. So this was how butterflies looked when they fell asleep. Warm, vulnerable, in need of a man's protection.

And sexy as hell.

That blunt thought made him wince. She might have had a point earlier in the evening when she'd caustically asked who was going to protect her from her bodyguard! Up until this moment he hadn't thought that was really going to be a problem. He was sure he could keep the relationship businesslike and professional.

Then she'd had to go and fix the cure for his "nightmare." Jake reached out a callused fingertip and touched the side of her cheek as she reclined against the peach-colored pillow. She stirred faintly beneath his touch but didn't waken. He ought to pick her up and carry her back to her bed and leave her there.

And he would do exactly that in a moment or two, he promised himself, leaning back against the pillow beside her. Without thinking about it, he draped an arm behind her head, propped his feet back up on the white table and let his own head fall back on the banquette pillow.

He was half-curious now, wondering if her "cure" had worked.

Cautiously he put out his free hand and used the television's remote-control mechanism to turn off the set. Sabrina moved faintly, her head sliding down against his shoulder. As if it were the most natural thing in the world, he cradled her a little closer. Then he drew in a long breath and switched off the lamp beside the couch. In an instant the room was plunged back into darkness.

Jake waited.

But nothing happened. The claustrophobic panic didn't return. Unconsciously he let out a long sigh, amazed at his own sense of relief, and his arm tightened a little around the woman at his side.

Yes, he'd take her back to her own bed and leave her there in a few minutes. Not just yet, though, because Jake knew what was really keeping the night panic at bay. It wasn't the hot milk or the silly nonsense of the television show.

It was the feel of the woman nestled against him.

3

〰〰〰〰〰

Dawn was just beginning to lighten the cloudy Portland sky when Sabrina stirred vaguely against the unfamiliar confinement of a man's arm and sleepily sought a more comfortable position.

It took a minute for the implications of her situation to sink into her drowsy brain. A man's arm? Vaguely she stretched out her foot and found it trapped beneath a much heavier one. Reality and memory came back slowly. She'd fallen asleep on the banquette after fixing that hot milk for her new bodyguard. And he, obviously, had fallen asleep beside her. Clearly her treatment had worked, perhaps a little too well.

Slowly she tried to untangle herself from the pinning weight of masculine arms and legs and found herself trapped between Jake and the pillow-lined back of the banquette. Delicately she pushed a little at his body, finding it warm and heavy alongside hers. She was folded into the curve of him, her head sharing the same pillow he used.

When the gentle prodding did not succeed in freeing her, Sabrina tried to turn so that she lay facing him. As she wriggled onto her side, she found him watching her intently from beneath half-lowered lashes.

Waking up to find that rain-colored gaze on her at the break of dawn was more of a shock than Sabrina would have guessed. It literally froze her into absolute motionlessness.

Desperately she sought for something witty to say, anything to break the thick, intense atmosphere which was suddenly swamping her. But the masculine awareness in those intelligent gray eyes was too overwhelming, too dangerous to allow for the light mockery she normally employed so easily. One didn't joke with a man who was looking at you with that kind of raw hunger in his eyes. One ran.

Except that she couldn't get free of him.

The jeans-clad leg along her thigh tightened and the callused hand tangled in her hair slowly clenched to hold her still, and then Jake lifted his head and deliberately brought his mouth down onto hers.

Sabrina's sleep-dazed senses accepted the inevitability of the kiss, surrendering to the hard, strangely demanding mouth that took hers completely. There in the pale light of dawn, trapped in the arms of a stranger, she made no attempt to resist the heavy onslaught of a kiss that was unlike anything she had ever experienced.

There was no playfulness, no teasing, probing inquiry behind this caress. He used none of the familiar seduction techniques which Sabrina would have found easy to resist. Instead she was crushed down into the pillows, held in the curve of a sinewy arm and feasted upon by a man whose hunger was too elemental to allow for any of the casual, sporting games men played so well.

When a man wasn't playing games, Sabrina discovered, a woman was helpless to resist.

Jake's mouth pried open her sleep-softened lips, seeking the warmth within and taking it for his own. The hard fingers in her hair splayed wide along the side of her head and down to her throat, sending tremors of sensual awareness through her limbs. When he felt the small shiver in her, Jake groaned far back in his throat and thrust his tongue deeply into her.

Sabrina's nails clenched involuntarily into the flesh of his shoulder as he invaded her mouth, and another uncertain tremor coursed through her. His callused palm moved down the line of her shoulder and below, finding the delicate curve of her breast through the fabric of the robe.

Sabrina was vividly aware of the rasp of his thumb as it sought the shape of her nipple, and when she moved restlessly beneath his touch, he used the solid power of his thighs to crush her hips down into the cushions. At once she was made to know the extent of his heavily aroused state. Even through the layers of clothing between them she was left in no doubt about it. The knowledge threatened to take away her breath.

At last his mouth shifted reluctantly, wrenching free of her lips to explore the line of her jaw up to the earlobe. Sabrina found herself gasping for air, her mind fogged, almost numbed.

"Jake? Jake, please, what are you doing? Wait, you must stop." She was silently appalled at the lack of strength in her words. The dawn was glowing brighter through the window, though, and the light of the day helped her gather her willpower. She pushed at his shoulder, gently at first and then a little harder. This had to stop and it was obvious she had to be the one to stop it.

Just as she was expecting to find herself engaged in a full-scale struggle which she was sure to lose, he muttered her name and something guttural which sounded like a stifled oath. The disgust, she sensed, was aimed at himself, not at her. Then he was pulling away, freeing her.

Raising his head, Jake gazed down at her, his hand still resting on her breast. She swallowed, wide-eyed and doubtful. She was certainly adult enough to understand how the kiss had gotten started. What Sabrina didn't comprehend was her own reaction to it.

The expression in his eyes was one of wariness and grim uncertainty. "That was my fault. I had no business taking advantage of you that way, Sabrina. For God's sake, I'm supposed to be protecting you!" He hesitated and then asked with a hint of defensive challenge, "Are you going to stage a major scene? Tell me I obviously can't be trusted as a bodyguard? Phone Teague or your mother and demand they find a replacement?"

Sabrina tried to gather her wits. "Can I?"

"Can you what?" he retorted huskily, eyeing her with a grave, assessing glance.

"Trust you as a bodyguard?" she quipped, determined not to let him stampede her into saying more than she wished in that moment. The truth was, she didn't know exactly what she wanted to do. Sabrina felt unsettled and out of focus, as if her world had suddenly shifted slightly but perceptibly. The shift was not enough to cause panic but it was enough to make her very uneasy.

She ought to be doing exactly as he'd gruffly suggested, telling her mother that the situation was intolerable and another bodyguard would have to be found.

Yet the idea of never seeing this man again was astoundingly depressing. She should be afraid of him or at least feel highly ambivalent about him. Sabrina no longer let men get as close as this one had almost gotten. It was much too dangerous.

Her barriers were firmly in place, though, she reminded herself. Hadn't she called a halt before things had gone too far? And he'd obeyed. She found herself clinging tenaciously to that last thought. He'd obeyed her demand to stop the lovemaking.

"You can trust me," Jake said evenly. "As a bodyguard."

"Then, as you once so succinctly observed," she declared, wriggling across his legs to stand up beside the banquette, "I guess we're still stuck with each other, aren't we?"

He reached out to snag her hand just as she would have fled in the general direction of the bathroom. "Sabrina! Wait a second. Are you . . . are you afraid of me?"

She looked down at her captured hand. "It's difficult to be afraid of a man who falls asleep over a mug of hot milk!"

He stared up at her for a split second and then a slow grin softened the hard planes of his face. "It was very nice to fall asleep. That was the first good night's sleep I've had in ages."

"You have nightmares often?" she asked sympathetically.

He shook his head. "It's not exactly a case of having nightmares." He released her hand suddenly, grimacing. "It's hard to explain and it's not really important. But thanks."

Sabrina edged toward the bath, part of her wanting to sit back down beside him and ask for an explanation. It was strange, this feeling of wanting to give comfort. She'd never met a man who seemed to need it. It was even stranger that now she had met one he should turn out to make his living doing something as supremely macho as teaching self-defense and acting as a bodyguard in his spare time. Just before she reached the hall, she turned and confronted him.

"Jake, there's one thing I think we should get clear between us."

"I know," he said quietly. "You don't want what happened this morning to happen again, right?"

"That's right. I realize that it was partly my fault this time. I should never have dropped off to sleep last night the way I did. Just the same, I'd like to make it plain that I'm not in the market for a lover or a vacation fling."

"You've made your point. Go take your shower." The words were a harsh growl. Sabrina hurried off to dress, feeling more confused than ever.

She was still unable to get the events of the evening off her mind half an hour later as she emerged from the shower and reached for her traveling clothes: a pair of white cotton pants, narrow at the ankle and cut full at the hip with lots of sassy pleats; and a trim white cotton blouse that set off her small figure. Stepping into white sandals, she added a tiny gold necklace to fill in the rather large expanse of skin left exposed by the partially unbuttoned blouse.

Then Sabrina checked her casually knotted hair in the mirror, picked up a white cotton duck shoulder bag and took a last glance around her bedroom. She was ready. Sailing out into the living room, she found that all signs of last night's disturbing fiasco had been cleared away. Everything was neat and tidy, the blankets and sheets folded and stacked on the white table. The sound of the shower told her the whereabouts of her bodyguard.

"There's time for breakfast before we have to leave to pick up your things and drive to the airport," she called out from the kitchen a few minutes later when the shower stopped.

"Sounds good. I didn't get any dinner last night," Jake remarked, arriving in her kitchen doorway a few minutes later. He was pulling the black knit shirt over his head and when his face emerged from the neck opening Sabrina was overly conscious of the feel of those gray eyes on her. "Except for the hot milk, of course," he added thoughtfully.

"No dinner! Why in the world didn't you eat? Do you skip a lot of meals?" she demanded disapprovingly as she bustled around the kitchen.

"Only when I'm traipsing after stubborn, willful lady clients who are deliberately trying to make my job harder." He smiled when she glanced up sharply.

"I'll try to remember to be more considerate of the hired help," she shot back very smoothly. "Sit down and eat!"

He did so, wolfing down the cereal and the last of the milk as if they were a choice omelet and a croissant. "I'm, uh, cleaning out the refrigerator, since I'll be gone for ten days," Sabrina felt obliged to explain as she, too, sat down to cereal and milk. She wished she wasn't feeling a nagging sense of guilt over having deprived him of his dinner the night before. After all, it was entirely his own fault!

When they were ready to depart at last, Sabrina once again picked up the white duck bag and slung it jauntily over her shoulder. The strap pulled at the material of her blouse slightly, making the deep V of the neckline a little wider.

From halfway across the room, Jake glanced at her and halted. His dark brows drew together in a surprisingly severe line as he paced deliberately back toward where she stood near the door.

"What's the matter?" Sabrina looked up at him inquiringly as he approached.

"As soon as you finish getting dressed, nothing will be the matter," he growled, and reached out to do up two of the three buttons she had left undone.

Startled by the totally unexpected possessiveness of the action, Sabrina stared at him, dumbfounded. "What in the world? Jake, stop that! What do you think you're doing?" She tried to step away but it was too late. He had very neatly fastened the buttons.

"I'm just seeing to it that the whole planeload of passengers doesn't learn that you don't believe in investing heavily in bras." He turned away again to pick up her luggage, leaving Sabrina too astonished to think of any of the scathing retorts he so richly deserved.

"You obviously know nothing about style!" she finally managed as he scooped up one of the suitcases and reached for the other.

"I may not know style but I do know flaunting," he returned easily.

"Flaunting!" Sabrina glared at him furiously. "Women my size can hardly be accused of *flaunting* anything!" Who in the world would ever accuse a size thirty-two A of flaunting herself? she wondered grimly.

"Women your size make men think of sleek, sensuous little cats," he drawled as he picked up the remaining suitcase. "It's a very sexy image, and believe me, if you walk into a plane with that blouse half-open, men are going to leer."

"Men like you!"

"Exactly. What the hell have you got in this suitcase?" he added, frowning down at the one he had just picked up.

"The books I'll need for the seminar." She smiled with relish. "Too heavy for you?" she added in a voice dripping with artificial sweetener. Served him right after his last remarks.

"I'll manage," he muttered grimly. "But didn't it occur to you to split up the books, half in one suitcase and half in the other?" He started toward the door.

"It did until I remembered I had a big strong body-guard along to assist in the luggage handling!" Sabrina checked all the lights and locked the door behind them.

In the underground garage she suddenly remembered she had never received her keys back from Jake. "What did you do with my keys after you kidnapped me last night?" She slid into the driver's seat of the MG and held out a hand expectantly as Jake finished stowing her cases.

"I've still got them." He walked up to stand beside the open door on the driver's side, eyeing her coolly as she extended her palm. "And since I intend to do the driving, I'm going to keep them. Move over, Sabrina," he ordered quite gently.

She considered the soft command, one nail tapping on the steering wheel as she glared up at him. "You're becoming awfully bossy," she finally observed.

"I've seen you drive," was all he said.

"And I've seen *you* drive. Get in on the passenger side, Jake, or get left behind," she advised. "I've got a spare set of keys in my purse."

"Sabrina—" he began firmly.

"I mean it, Jake." And suddenly she did. Very much.

He seemed to sense the determination in her. One brow arched quizzically as if he were considering the alternatives, and then without a word he closed her car door, paced around the hood and slid into the passenger seat. His own door shut very gently.

Sabrina smiled, feeling back in control, and started the engine. Other than to give her the address of his apartment Jake didn't say a thing as she whipped the little sports car through the streets. He endured the flashy, reckless driving with an expression of utter fatalism. Sabrina was laughing at him with her eyes when she brought the MG to a flourishing halt in front of the old brick apartment building.

"Are we even now?" Jake asked politely as they got out of the car and walked toward the door.

"Even?" she inquired innocently.

"You said last night you'd get even for the, uh, lesson I taught you, right?" he reminded her as they climbed a flight of worn stairs. "I just want to know if I can consider myself punished."

"By my driving? Heavens no, Jake. I always drive like that," she chuckled, and stepped inside the stark one-room apartment he called home.

"I'll just be a minute," he murmured, and strode across the bare floor to haul out a canvas bag from under the daybed.

Sabrina glanced around, startled at the barren, cold feel of the place. Everything was neat, chillingly so, and very clean, but there had been no effort to soften the sparsely furnished room. There were no homey touches and no sign of any money to spare for them. Instantly she felt contrite. Jake Devlin, apparently, really did need this job.

"Ready?" she asked with deliberate cheerfulness as he finished dropping a few pairs of socks and some other odds and ends into the canvas bag and zipped it shut.

"Ready. But this time I'm doing the driving, Sabrina. I've been punished enough," he declared implacably. Sabrina decided not to argue.

* * *

An hour into the long flight to Hawaii, Sabrina looked up from her copy of Sir Thomas Malory's *Morte d'Arthur* to find her bodyguard reading over her shoulder.

"That's what you're going to be studying in Hawaii?" Jake asked curiously as she gave him an inquiring glance. "The tales of King Arthur?"

"Ummm. And how they were used during the Middle Ages to support and teach the ideals of chivalry. Fascinating stuff. Do you know the legend?"

He shrugged. "Everyone knows the basic story, I guess. Part of our Western culture. It's been a while since I read the tales, though. I seem to remember a lot of knightly deeds and quests for Holy Grails or something."

"And the wonderful romantic part about Lancelot and Guenevere? Do you remember that part, too?" she teased lightly. "Or do males just concentrate on the knightly deeds of valor?"

He gave her an odd look. "Oh, I remember the part about Lancelot and Guenevere. Arthur should have kept a tighter rein on his queen. Because of her and Lancelot, everything he'd built was destroyed in the end."

"Hey, wait a minute," Sabrina protested. "That's not fair. It all ended tragically, but it wasn't Lancelot's or Guenevere's fault!"

"Sure it was. If Guenevere had been faithful to Arthur instead of fooling around with Lancelot—" he began seriously.

"She didn't *fool* around with Lancelot!" Sabrina cried, incensed. "It was a great chivalric love! All the knights were expected to honor and give service to a lady. Lancelot was the greatest knight in Arthur's kingdom. It was right that he should honor and serve the greatest lady of that kingdom!"

"Who just happened to be Arthur's wife," Jake pointed out dryly. "The wife of his lord and his friend."

"Well, that was the way chivalry worked," Sabrina tried to explain. "A knight was expected to love a lady from afar, and it didn't matter whether or not she was married. The important thing was that the desire to please her impelled him to do great deeds in her honor. It provided a knight with the overwhelming wish to better himself, to become a great hero, be the best possible sort of knight. Medieval knights always yearned to serve a lady, but the whole idea was to worship her from afar, to take inspiration from her—not to sleep with her!"

"Lancelot," Jake stated incontrovertibly, "slept with Guenevere."

"Malory doesn't say that," Sabrina argued. "He says he doesn't claim to know whether or not they were in bed together when Mordred surprised Lancelot in the queen's chamber. What counts is that Mordred told the king he'd found them together and that Guenevere had betrayed Arthur with his favorite knight. Once her reputation had been ruined, Arthur was forced to act. He had to condemn her to death because that was the law. And Lancelot, as Arthur probably knew full well, had to rescue her."

"And in so doing the kingdom was torn apart," Jake concluded. "Like I said, Arthur should have kept a tighter rein on Guenevere."

"Dammit, you can't simplify a great tragedy that way! Lancelot and Guenevere were probably never lovers in the physical sense."

"They were."

She gave him a fulminating glance. "You don't know that."

"I know the male of the species, remember? Or have you forgotten already that I am one? Men don't tend to worship very long from afar, not if they can get inside the queen's bedchamber, believe me. Lancelot and Guenevere were guilty of betraying Arthur. Take my word for it."

"Take your word for it!" Sabrina echoed, outraged. "Why should I take your word for it? Have you studied Malory? Have you researched the concept of medieval chivalry? What do you know about chivalric love?"

Jake turned his head to give her a steady, absolutely certain glance. "I know," he said quietly, "that a man can want a woman physically without feeling any particularly noble emotional commitment to her. But I also know that if he does feel a noble emotional commitment, if he *needs* her, wants to serve her, then he's also going to want to possess her physically. Which is why chivalry never worked all that well in practice."

Sabrina gave up and slammed her book shut. "I can see this is a pointless discussion. If you'll excuse me, I'm going to take a hike around this plane and stretch my legs."

"The rest room," he informed her with a trace of humor, "is behind us about fifteen rows."

"Thanks," she muttered dryly, scrambling past his long legs.

Actually, for perhaps the first time in recent memory, Sabrina was running from an intellectual argument and she knew it. But she couldn't help it. The discussion was getting far too dangerous. All she had been able to think about while Jake described a man's responses was the way he had been responding to her on the banquette that morning. It was, quite literally, the very last memory she wished to have revived because along with it came the recollection of her own reaction to his elemental lovemaking. She quickened her pace toward the rest rooms.

It was as she was deliberately dawdling back down the aisle that she spotted the man with the horn-rimmed glasses and the sandy brown hair sitting about ten rows behind her own seat. She spotted him because he, too, was reading an edition of Malory's *Morte d'Arthur*. There could be only one reason for such a coincidence. Sabrina leaned over the edge of the high-backed plane seat and smiled cheerfully. "Excuse me, but you wouldn't by any chance be going to Hawaii to attend a vacation seminar on chivalry, would you?"

The young man glanced up in surprise. Then he removed the horn-rimmed glasses and began polishing them with what appeared to be an absent habit as he smiled back bashfully. "Why, yes, I am. You too?"

Sabrina extended her hand and found it lightly taken and politely held for a few seconds. It was returned uncrushed, she reflected as she introduced herself glibly. Not at all the way it had been returned the last time she had extended it to be shaken by a man!

"I'm very happy to meet you, Sabrina. I'm Perry Dryden." He struggled up out of the seat, apparently conscious of his manners.

As soon as he stood to his full height beside her, Sabrina's smile broadened happily. Instantly she knew she was going to like Perry Dryden very much. He was barely two inches taller than herself. Since she was wearing high-heeled sandals, they met eye to eye. What a pleasure not to have to crane one's neck to talk to a man. What a joy not to feel overwhelmed physically. What a satisfaction it was to meet a man on her own level.

"I see you're doing a little studying," she said, indicating the book he'd let fall back into the seat. "I've been doing the same. It should be a fascinating vacation, don't you think?"

Polite, a trifle shy, anxious to be friends, Perry Dryden proved more than eager to discuss their forthcoming venture. Sabrina had time to discover that he was an officer in a Portland escrow office and that the study of the Arthurian legend and the Age of Chivalry had been a passion of Perry's since high school—before they were interrupted by Jake's gritty drawl.

"There you are, Sabrina. Hard to believe anyone could get lost between her seat and the rest room."

"Hard to believe anyone would consider it necessary to come looking," she murmured. "There wasn't much chance of me really getting lost, was there? Jake, I'd like you to meet Perry Dryden. He's going to the seminar too!"

Jake nodded aloofly at the shorter, younger man and then he put a hand under Sabrina's elbow. "Let's get back to our seats, Sabrina. They're serving coffee and a snack."

Perry looked awkward and a little confused. "Are you and Jake traveling together?" he asked, clearing his throat. He didn't look at Jake for the answer, but that was the direction from which it came.

"Yes," Devlin announced flatly. "We are. Let's go, Sabrina."

"I'll be along in a few minutes, Jake," she told him severely. Then she turned back to Perry. "Don't mind him, he's just a friend of the family who decided to come along with me because he needs a vacation," she explained airily.

"I see," Perry said a little blankly.

"Here comes the coffee wagon," Jake noted, glancing back toward their seats. His fingers did something unexpected and a little devastating to the soft nerve center above Sabrina's elbow. She gasped, not from pain but from a nerve-tingling little shock. The next thing she knew, she was obediently allowing herself to be led back up the aisle.

"What did you do?" she hissed, massaging her elbow half-curiously.

"Did I hurt you?" Jake was suddenly extremely solicitous.

"Well, no, not exactly, but . . ." She slid him a suspicious sideways glance and gave up trying to make an accusation stick. Already her elbow felt fine again. It might have been an accident that his fingers had found just that spot and produced that odd sensation. In any event, she had a hunch Jake wasn't going to admit to a thing. "Never mind." She sank down into her seat. "Did you have to be so rude to Perry? He was very nice."

"Didn't anyone ever tell you not to talk to strangers?" Jake dropped lithely down into the aisle seat and fastened his seat belt again.

"The only warning I ever got was to be on the lookout for tall, dark strangers," she said crisply, reaching for her copy of Malory. "Like you. Short men like Perry Dryden are much safer!"

"Even a knight with all of Lancelot's virtues didn't turn out to be particularly safe. Just ask King Arthur."

"Lancelot was probably tall," Sabrina muttered.

4

~~~~~~~~~~~

The magnificent resort on the island of Hawaii reigned over an endless stretch of beach. Miles from the nearest town, the sprawling hotel gleamed brilliantly in the setting sun late that afternoon. The location was one of isolated grandeur, offering guests seclusion and all the amenities they could possibly wish. Golf course, restaurants, tennis courts, pools, first-class service and, of course, the fabulous beach were all carefully planned to satisfy the most demanding guest. The vast, empty reaches of island around the hotel gave one the illusion of being truly in a world apart.

"Was it hard getting the front desk to give you a room on the same floor as mine?" Sabrina asked Jake as the bellhop led them to her door.

"No, the hard part was getting them to give us adjoining rooms." Jake followed her into the elegantly appointed suite, his gaze going immediately to the inner connecting door.

"Adjoining rooms!" Sabrina swung around, startled, and then closed her mouth until the bellhop had been tipped and dismissed. "Was that strictly necessary?"

"I'm supposed to be within shouting distance, remember?" he asked laconically as he began prowling around the room, examining windows and locks.

"Believe me, I can yell quite loudly. You won't have to be this close in order to hear me!"

"You didn't do much yelling last night when I picked you up at your friend's party." He prodded the lock on the sliding glass door that opened onto the balcony. They were three floors above ground level, overlooking the beach.

"You had your hand over my mouth," she reminded him, irritated.

"Exactly. Now, if you'll excuse me, I'll change for that welcome party you're supposed to attend before dinner." Jake moved through the connecting door, leaving it open behind him.

"I suppose I should be grateful you aren't going to wear a shoulder holster with your aloha shirt," she sighed.

"I'm just damned grateful this is Hawaii and I'm not expected to dress formally," he called back grimly. "Otherwise Teague would have had to get your mother to rent me an entire wardrobe!"

Sabrina went to stand in the doorway, curious. "Aren't you armed at all? I mean, I know you told me yesterday that you weren't going to carry anything as tacky as a gun, but aren't bodyguards supposed to have some sort of weapon?"

"I'll take care of you, Sabrina," he told her neutrally,

unzipping the canvas bag he had brought along. "Go get dressed for the cocktail party." He shot her a hooded glance. "Unless you'd rather stand there and watch me get dressed?"

He might not own an Italian-cut evening jacket or a silk shirt with his initials monogrammed on the pocket, Sabrina decided forty minutes later as she walked to the poolside party with him, but on a body as tough and lean and coordinated as Jake's, anything looked good. The khaki shirt and light-colored jeans he wore suited the relaxed atmosphere of the Hawaiian evening but they didn't have the aura casual leisure clothes usually had. On Jake they looked like the kind of thing he probably wore every day. Even the heavy leather belt with its solid brass buckle looked well worn rather than stylish. His hair was rather closely cropped compared to the styles being worn by the other men in the vicinity, giving him a vaguely military look.

Standing beside Jake's lean, supple body, aware of the uncompromisingly solid strength under the khaki shirt and jeans, Sabrina felt even smaller than usual. She was wearing a little silk dress, all flounces and flirty neckline, done in a rainbow of jewel colors. Sabrina was wishing she'd worn something more dynamic and assertive when a rising murmur of conversation greeted the arrival of their instructor.

Sabrina swung around just as Jake was politely thrusting a frosty glass of rum-based punch into her fingers. It was the first time she'd seen Dr. Larissa Waverly, and her comment to Jake came out before she could pause to think.

"So you think you know flaunting? *That's* flaunting!"

Her wry outrage surprised a smile from Jake, who turned to follow her glance. "Medieval scholars have changed since I was in college," he murmured.

Dr. Waverly swept into the patio area with a natural sense of the dramatic that Sabrina could only admire. She was a beautiful woman, tall, voluptuously proportioned and dressed to display the fact. There was nothing medieval about the cut of the body-molding sundress worn by the good doctor. It revealed cleavage belonging to a thirty-six C at least. Sabrina's mouth continued to curve into a wry twist as she watched the professor make her way through the crowd of sixty or so medieval enthusiasts. The overhead lights strung around the pool gleamed on her shoulder-length red hair and Sabrina was sure her beautifully shaped eyes were going to turn out to be very green.

"There's flaunting and there's flaunting," Jake said cryptically.

"You can say that again. Well, I guess Dr. Waverly won't have any trouble keeping the attention of the male students, at least." Before Sabrina could say anything else, the beautiful professor was upon them, all charm and self-confident grace.

"I'm so glad you decided to join our little group at the last minute, Jake," the woman murmured with a deliciously husky voice as the introductions were made. In her high-heeled sandals she was only a couple of inches shorter than he and Sabrina was inexplicably uncomfortable at the realization that the other two looked quite attractive together.

"Thank you," Jake returned politely. "I'm looking forward to the seminars."

"Have you been interested in the subject for long?" Dr. Waverly inquired.

For some reason Jake slanted a short, meaningful glance at Sabrina's carefully composed features before answering smoothly, "No, not long. Sabrina, here, is the one who inspired my, uh, enthusiasm."

"Don't let him fool you, Dr. Waverly," Sabrina felt obliged to add sweetly as she recalled the discussion on the jet. "Jake has some strongly formulated opinions on the Arthurian legends!"

"Does he really?" Larissa Waverly seemed excited at the prospect. "We'll look forward to hearing them in class. I must move along now and say hello to the others. See you later, Jake, Sabrina." She drifted off in a cloud of flowery perfume.

Jake cast a quelling glance down at Sabrina. "I'd appreciate it if you would refrain from getting me involved in scholarly discussions. I'm only going to be attending those classes so that I can keep an eye on you. I'd just as soon not be called upon to sound scholarly and informed in the process!"

"Sorry," she retorted irrepressibly. "I thought you might enjoy impressing Dr. Waverly."

"Whatever gave you that idea?"

"Something about the way she was flaunting herself in front of you, I suppose." Sabrina grinned. She held out her empty glass. "Would you mind getting me another . . ." Before she could finish the request, a cool glass full of rum punch was being helpfully thrust toward her and she turned to find Perry Dryden standing a little diffidently to one side.

"Excuse me," he said, sounding anxious. "But I noticed yours was getting empty and I happened to be going past the punch table at the time."

"Why, thank you," Sabrina said, setting down her empty glass and accepting the one he offered. "How nice of you."

"Very perceptive," Jake drawled in his grittiest tones. "But I think Sabrina's had enough on an empty stomach." He deftly plucked the rum drink from her fingers and turned a hooded expression on the reddening Perry

Dryden. "If you'll excuse us, we were just going in to dinner."

"Yes, yes, of course." Perry nodded quickly, stepping back. His gaze, half-hopeful, half-melancholy, followed Sabrina as she was led firmly away.

"Jake!" she snapped furiously. "Stop this at once! I don't know what you think you're doing by being so rude to poor Perry, but I won't tolerate any more of this behavior! Kindly remember that you work for me!"

"Your friend Dryden is picturing himself in the role of Lancelot, I think," Jake declared in low tones as he led her away from the chattering crowd and off toward the open-air hotel dining room. "But I don't intend to make Arthur's mistake of leaving his queen unprotected."

Sabrina drew in an astonished breath, her eyes widening angrily. "Don't get me wrong," she muttered caustically. "I think it's just wonderful the way you're getting into the spirit of this vacation, but I'm not about to let you get that carried away with your role playing!"

"My role is to protect you, Sabrina," he said.

"Not from people like Perry Dryden!"

"From anyone I think you need protecting from," he countered ruthlessly, drawing to a halt in front of the maître d'. Sabrina was unable to say anything further as they were led to a seat overlooking the ocean. By the time they had ordered fresh mahimahi, basil and zucchini salad and a California Chardonnay wine which Sabrina selected based on what she had learned in the wine seminar she had taken, it was difficult to revive the full force of her displeasure. When Jake gallantly told the waiter to present the wine to her for the tasting ritual, her annoyance faded completely. Most of the men she dated wouldn't have had the self-confidence to forgo the traditionally masculine prerogative.

But she was learning that Jake Devlin didn't fit into any convenient category.

"So what did you do before you moved to Portland last year and established the self-defense school for kids?" Sabrina asked curiously halfway through the meal.

"I did some overseas work for the government," he told her blandly, helping himself to a crusty roll and slathering it with butter.

"What sort of work? And don't use too much butter. The cholesterol isn't good for you."

He grinned and popped a piece of the roll, butter and all, into his mouth. "Oh, the usual bureaucratic shuffling around. A lot of paperwork and a lot of travel. You're a real fund of miscellaneous information, aren't you? What else are you an expert on besides wine, the sleep-inducing properties of milk and the hazards of cholesterol?"

She ignored that, deciding to stick to priorities. "What made you decide to give up the government work?"

"I felt like a career change," he replied dryly. "What about you? Have you always been a librarian?"

"Oh, yes. I got my degree in history and a master's in library science the year after I graduated from college. Went right into academic librarianship. I love it. The perfect excuse to delve into almost any subject under the sun."

"Which is how you acquire so many odd facts, I suppose." He nodded and then remarked with suspicious coolness, "Teague said you'd been married for a year."

Sabrina glanced up warily, startled. "Did your friend Teague give you a complete rundown on me?"

"Just a few facts." Jake shrugged, his gray eyes steady

on her suddenly remote ones. "He just said you'd married briefly and that you'd been divorced."

"Yes."

"What happened?"

"I prefer not to discuss it," she said briefly.

"That bad, huh?" There was a genuine note of sympathy in his voice.

"Let's just say it was a learning experience," she retorted wryly.

"People tend to use that expression when they emerge from a situation somewhat the worse for wear," he observed quietly.

"It's not really any of your business, is it, Jake?"

"It could be," he astonished her by saying. "Your mother told Teague that she didn't trust your ex-husband one bit after what he did to you two years ago. She thinks he's a likely candidate for the role of bad guy in this mess."

"What!" Sabrina nearly dropped her fork in amazement. "Stan involved in making threats to my mother's company? Not a chance!"

"You sound very certain of that," he mused.

"I am. I lived with the man for a year. I know him quite well, unfortunately. Take my word for it, he wouldn't be involved in anything like this," she stated emphatically.

"How can you be so sure?"

Sabrina's voice hardened as she recalled the image of her handsome, sophisticated ex-husband. "Stan Northrup is the quintessential user of people. I got in his path and I got used. But he's incapable of making any kind of meaningful commitment, including the revolutionary or political one which would seem to be required of the type of person involved in threatening my mother's company."

"On what do you base that?" The question was so gentle, so unthreatening that Sabrina found herself answering it before she stopped to think.

"His father owned a large company in Seattle. He wanted Stan to settle down and get married before he would let him take over control of the firm. Stan wanted to take over from his father, so he looked around for a simpleminded sort of female who could be seduced into marriage."

"And found you?"

"I met him at a party being given by some friends," Sabrina sighed. "I thought it was a case of love at first sight. I was still rather romantically inclined in those days," she added apologetically. " 'Stupid' might be a better word. At any rate I thought he needed me, loved me, and I agreed to marry him. Well, he did need me. He needed me to convince his father he was settled and ready to take over the firm. His father thought I was terrific, which made everything very pleasant. Then his father died unexpectedly."

"And Northrup no longer needed you?"

"He much preferred to live an uncommitted sort of life," Sabrina said flatly. "When I came home one day to find him in bed with his secretary, I took the initiative and left him. It suited everyone for me to be gone. He's not a very nice man, Jake, but he's definitely not the sort to be mixed up in something like this, believe me." For an instant memories of her husband's casual, unemotional lust returned to swamp her mind, but Sabrina thrust them aside. "I can't understand why my mother or Teague would have considered him a viable possibility for the villain in this."

Jake just looked at her, saying nothing, and suddenly the truth hit Sabrina. Her eyes widened in glittering fury. "My God! You tricked me, didn't you? Neither Teague nor my mother mentioned Stan as a threat, did they? You just wanted to know more about him than I seemed willing to tell you!"

"I was curious," he admitted softly, eyes unfathomable as he watched her taut features.

"I can't imagine why!" she blazed.

"Can't you?"

She picked up her fork, simultaneously taking a grip on her flaring temper. She would not let this man push her into making a fool of herself. "I thought I made it clear this morning, Jake, that I am not in the market for an affair. I meant it. Don't misread that unfortunate little episode on the banquette at dawn!"

"Unfortunate little episode," he repeated thoughtfully. "That's not how I remember it. Sabrina, I had the first good night's sleep I've had in ages last night because of you."

"Is that why you kissed me? You were feeling grateful?" she challenged.

"No. It was a lot more complicated than that."

"There's nothing complicated about it! You told me yourself that men don't have to feel any noble emotional commitment before they go to bed with a woman. Believe me, I'm already aware of that fact. Let's drop the subject, shall we?"

He shrugged. "If that's what you want."

"It is."

"Just remember I also said that a man who does feel some sort of chivalric commitment to a woman is also going to want to possess her."

She smiled very brilliantly. "In other words, a poor girl won't be able to tell the noble ones from the ignoble ones, will she? Clearly her best bet is not to let any of them too close. As you keep telling me, Jake, one can't be too careful."

Secure in the knowledge that she'd put him firmly in his place, Sabrina didn't hesitate to reinforce the lesson after dinner when they moved into the crowded lounge. She politely but firmly refused his invitation to dance.

"Sabrina," Jake began wearily, "you know damn well you want to dance. Why in hell are you punishing yourself? Just for the satisfaction of punishing me?"

Before she had to answer that question, Sabrina was rescued by Perry Dryden, who self-consciously edged his way up to the table and, after a wary glance at Jake's forbidding face, mumbled an invitation to Sabrina.

Sensing the sheer guts and determination it must have taken for him to work up the nerve, Sabrina smiled kindly and got to her feet at once. "Thank you, Perry, I'd love to." Without a backward glance at Jake, she allowed herself to be guided out onto the dance floor, which was open to the balmy evening breezes.

As soon as her new escort took her into his arms, Sabrina relaxed and began to enjoy herself. What a pleasure it was to feel like a *partner* on the dance floor instead of a short, lightweight appendage to be hauled around at the whim of someone much taller and stronger. With Perry she could really dance. And he turned out to be surprisingly skillful at it. When he, too, began to relax, they turned out to be a natural couple. Their steps became increasingly intricate and Sabrina's mood had lightened immeasurably after only a few minutes.

When the music came to a close, Perry outdid himself by spinning her around into a dramatic little whirl, and Sabrina found herself laughing with delight. Perry, too, was flushed with pleasure as he gallantly escorted her back to the table where Jake waited. The younger man's confidence deserted him, however, as the waiting man rose to claim Sabrina.

"This next dance is mine, I believe," Jake drawled,

taking hold of her arm before she could sit down. "Good night, Dryden."

Perry took the dismissal civilly, pausing to wish Sabrina a proper good evening.

"Thank you, Perry. That was fun."

"I enjoyed it too," he replied, much of his pleasure clearly restored by her gratitude. Then he disappeared in the crowd. A man of his stature tended to disappear quickly in a group of people.

"Come on, Sabrina." Jake started resolutely toward the dance floor, ignoring the way she was trying to literally dig in her heels.

"I don't care to dance again, Jake," she managed haughtily, and then found herself hauled effortlessly into his arms as they reached the floor. "That was the nice thing about dancing with Perry," she complained as he trapped her within the confines of his arms and began to move to the music. "He was exactly the right height for me!"

"And you," Jake stated, nuzzling her soft hair appreciatively, "are exactly the right height for me!"

There was nothing intricate or fancy about his dancing, Sabrina reflected after a moment, but there was a remarkably fluid, coordinated feel to it. It struck her that with his martial-arts training Jake probably had a smoothly developed coordination that would see him through anything, from an act of violence to an act of love. The coupling of the two extremes in her mind sent a shiver down the length of her spine.

He must have felt it, because his palm moved deliberately on her back, finding as if by accident the delicate spot in the region just above her hips. There his fingers seemed to know exactly how to work the sensitive nerve endings. Sabrina shivered again and this time there was a sensuous thrill in the sensation, which was something of a shock for her. Uncertainly, she remained quiescent in his grasp, saying nothing until the dance was over. When he walked her back to the table, she felt oddly dazed.

They went back to their rooms a couple of hours later, Sabrina claiming exhaustion from the effects of the long flight. Jake didn't protest but he went through an inspection of her room before walking toward the connecting door to his own.

"Good night, Sabrina," he said, turning to face her with his hand on the doorjamb. His eyes swept over her with an expression that made her glad she'd called a halt to the evening. The three dances she'd had with him that night had underlined what she had sensed that morning.

The man who was supposed to be protecting her wanted her.

Deliberately, chin lifted challengingly, she walked forward and started to close the connecting door. Jake backed a step into his room, his eyes never leaving hers. "Don't lock it, Sabrina."

"No," she agreed, knowing that for professional reasons he couldn't allow a locked door between them. But for symbolic reasons she had to at least close it. And she did so. "Good night, Jake."

Sabrina discovered that her fingers were trembling when she removed them from the doorknob. Very carefully, as if she'd had too much to drink, which wasn't the case at all, she got ready for bed. She was grateful for the swift, easy sleep which overtook her almost at once.

The same unidentifiable instinct that had aroused her the night before began to nibble at the edges of her mind almost two hours after Sabrina had fallen asleep.

She stirred briefly, coming slowly awake in the sea-scented hotel room, to find herself lying in a pool of moonlight. Turning her head on the pillow, she could see that the silvery pool was only a dab left over from the wide, glittering slash of moonlight that painted the ocean. A magic night in the islands, she told herself dreamily. A beautiful, fragrant Hawaiian night. Her gaze moved sleepily around the room and came to rest on the connecting door, which was wide open.

Sabrina blinked and then sat up, clutching the sheet to her throat as she frowned at the open door into Jake's room. He'd done it deliberately, of course. That door certainly hadn't opened on its own! But there was no sign of Jake. Through the doorway she could see his rumpled bed bathed in moonlight, as was her own. He wasn't in it.

Sitting very still for a timeless moment, Sabrina told herself that the best thing she could do was go back to sleep. To go looking for Jake tonight was to go looking for trouble of the kind she most certainly didn't need. Hadn't she learned her lesson last night?

Yet some nebulous, restless emotion seemed to be taking hold of her as she sat staring into the vacant room beyond her own. Where was he? Was he having another sleepless night?

Perhaps he'd gone out onto his balcony. The night before, he'd opened the door onto her balcony in Portland, claiming he'd wanted fresh air. Slowly, not giving herself time to really think it through any further, Sabrina slid one leg off the edge of the bed. In another couple of seconds she was standing, the night breeze through her open window gently playing with the long skirts of her apricot-colored nightgown. Reaching for the matching lightweight nylon travel robe, she slipped it on and tied the sash. There was still no sound from the adjoining room.

The nightmares, Sabrina reminded herself anxiously. A bad one must have gotten to him again. It was strange to contemplate the notion of her stern-faced bodyguard suffering from such a problem. But she'd never forgotten how devastating the unpredictable terrors of the mind could be. The urge to comfort drove her closer to the open door between the two rooms.

On the threshold she paused and glanced warily around. As she had suspected, Jake wasn't there, either in the bed or sitting in a chair. But his balcony door was open and she could see him leaning on the rail, the hard planes of his jaw and cheek silvered in the moonlight. He was staring out toward the sea, clad only in his jeans. One bare foot was lodged on the lowest bar.

Hesitantly Sabrina moved forward. "Jake?" Her voice was a whisper of sound.

"It's okay, Sabrina. Go back to bed." He didn't turn to look at her, but she thought the muscles across his bare shoulders tightened fractionally.

"Another nightmare?" she persisted softly, her compassion welling up to fill her voice.

"I said it's okay, Sabrina. Please go back to bed."

The fact that he wouldn't even turn around to look at her as he spoke was the deciding factor as far as Sabrina was concerned. Coming to a firm decision, she moved out onto the balcony beside him, her tawny brows drawing together in a determined line. "Jake, it doesn't get any better when you try to fight it alone. Not when the dreams are really bad. I don't care if you are thirty-five years old and make your living doing macho-type things like bodyguarding. Have you ever talked these dreams out with anyone?"

He didn't move, seemingly frozen in space beside her. "No."

"Then I think it's time you did. Tell me about them."

"Sabrina, I don't want . . ." He broke off and tried again. "There's no point. And you're not making things easier by standing here beside me in a nightgown," he added grimly.

"Forget about the nightgown, Jake." She touched his arm and was appalled at the tension lying in the muscles under his bare skin. "Tell me what it is that keeps you from sleeping. I want to know."

"Do you, butterfly? Do you really want to know?" he rasped, still staring straight ahead at the moonlit ocean.

Butterfly? Sabrina ignored the label, intent on other things at the moment. Keeping her hand on his arm, she stroked him gently as if he were a wild animal to be soothed and tamed. "Tell me about the dreams, Jake."

She sensed something give inside him. Some barrier that had been exceedingly well built but which had contained a treacherous hairline crack. For some reason tonight she had been assigned the task of putting more force on that crack than the surrounding structure could withstand. Jake still didn't move, but a fierce shudder went through him. Instantly Sabrina moved closer, her fingertips conveying her compassion and concern.

For a long time there was silence, and then Jake said haltingly, "It's not exactly a dream, Sabrina. It's a kind of panic." There was self-disgust in his voice and she sensed what it cost him to admit it. "Have you ever had claustrophobia?"

"I suppose everyone has had a touch of it at one time or another. A fear of being in a tight, confined space isn't all that rare, Jake."

"How about when the tight, confined space is very real and you can't escape? When the brick walls are damp with slime and there are small things living in there with you?" he rasped harshly. "When the heat builds up and doesn't dissipate at night and you wonder if you'll cook to death."

"Jake!" she cried, stricken.

He did turn and look at her then, and she was shocked at the bottomless gray seas of his eyes. Instinctively her hands moved to cradle his face, and her own gaze held the boundless comfort only a woman can give to a man.

"Sabrina . . ."

"Tell me the rest, Jake. You have to tell me everything now. Don't you see?"

He drew a short, ragged breath, standing unnaturally still under the touch of her hands. "It was a prison cell, Sabrina. A hellhole of a place in Southeast Asia. I was there for six months and I thought I was going to die there," he whispered starkly. His gray eyes burned over her as if seeking salvation. "The dying, I could have handled. It was staying sane that took everything I had."

"My God, Jake." It was a prayer.

"But I managed it," he went on heavily. "I refought every unarmed-combat match I'd ever been in, dissected every self-defense hold and the philosophy behind it that I'd ever learned and analyzed everything I'd ever known about willpower and energy. Then I started looking for the essentials of both the physical and the mental aspects, looking for ways of tying them together. I spent days, weeks, *months* shaping something unique in my head. A system of self-defense that was as much a part of the mind as it was of the body. And then I used that system to keep myself sane."

Sabrina's palms tightened gently around his hard face as she looked up at him with tenderness. After a moment Jake seemed to gather himself for the rest of the story.

"It was very close at times, butterfly," he said grimly. "There were nights when I thought the fear would win. Then, six months after I'd been caught and stuck in that hole, I got a chance to escape. The man who . . . who fed me once a day got careless."

Sabrina waited. "What happened, Jake?"

"He's dead and I'm here. That's what happened."

"Was it Vietnam?"

"No. Another place. One that doesn't matter anymore."

It all had to come out. Sabrina had to know everything. "What were you doing there?"

He closed his eyes briefly. "I told you I'd worked for the government."

"Yes?"

"Well, I was sort of a courier. Only I wasn't carrying diplomatic pouches. I carried other things. Like gold to finance resistance movements in that part of the world," he explained bleakly. "And two years ago things went wrong on one of the runs. A man we had been forced to trust . . ." Jake didn't finish, lifting one hand eloquently.

"He betrayed you?" she concluded in a tight voice.

"It had happened before, but this time I was a little slow realizing things had fallen apart. I took a chance. The wrong people were waiting for me when I brought the gold in that night."

"Thank God you weren't killed!" she breathed.

"I was being saved for a propaganda trial. From that standpoint I was lucky. They didn't do much to me physically because they didn't want me to look bad in the photos and on camera. It didn't matter how my mind looked, of course."

"So they used that to break you instead of the physical torture. Oh, my God, Jake."

"That's all there is." He lifted one shoulder in an attempt at a dismissing shrug. "I survived and I escaped. But at night . . ." He let the sentence trail off meaningfully.

"At night that feeling of being trapped in a closed room returns?"

He nodded bleakly. "Not as bad as it was then, of course. But bad enough. Bad enough. The worst part is that I can't seem to defeat it. No matter how I fight it mentally, it always returns. Sooner or later, the panic comes back. All I can do is turn on a light, get some fresh air, get out of the room I'm in. Those methods will dispel it, but they aren't very sleep-promoting! I don't understand it, Sabrina," he finished bleakly. "I found the willpower to keep myself sane for six months in that damn hole, and now I can't find enough strength to keep the memories at bay!"

"I think it must be because the stakes are different now, Jake," she murmured carefully. "When it was a life-and-death situation, a question of keeping your sanity or becoming a vegetable, you had to use everything you had to fight back, and you did. But here, back in real life, where only the memories hound you . . ."

"I can't draw on the same strength I did then?" he hazarded.

"Drawing on that kind of strength must be enormously draining for the body and the mind," she suggested. "Deep down inside, you know there's no longer a genuine threat, so perhaps your mind simply refuses to obey when you try to summon the same kind of resistance you used in that jail cell. Oh, Jake, I'm no expert. I don't know. And the experts probably don't know either. I know that when my father went away for good, taking all the fun and excitement out of my childhood, I found the strength to handle it. But I couldn't find the strength to handle the nightmares which plagued me for months afterward. Someone else had to help me do that."

"Your mother?"

"Yes. Maybe fighting these kinds of battles requires a little assistance from someone who cares." She smiled tremulously.

"Are you feeling maternal?" he growled, searching her face.

"Not in the least," she admitted, aware of him in every fiber of her body. "But I care, Jake. I know what the panic is like. I've never entirely forgotten."

Wordlessly she led him across to the wide chaise longue on the balcony, sitting down and tugging him down beside her. When he obeyed, she leaned back against the pillow.

But when she tried to cradle him beside her, intending to soothe him into sleep, Jake ceased to follow the guidance of her hands. He shifted his weight slightly, leaning over her and bracing himself on his palms on either side of her body.

"Sabrina, I'm not looking for a mother's care tonight." The masculine warning was plain now in his voice. "But I need you. I want you. And if you stay out here on this balcony a moment longer, I'm going to take you. You've driven the panic out of my mind, just as you did last night. But what has taken its place may be something to cause you to panic."

"Jake, please, I . . ." She didn't know what to say. A chattering little voice was beginning to shout at her to get off the chaise longue and return to her own room. Yet the compassion and tenderness she had been feeling were still terribly strong and they seemed to be combining with the physical sensations she had known earlier in his arms on the dance floor.

Sabrina hesitated, staring up at the man leaning over her. Jake's gray eyes gleamed like the silver out on the ocean, and then he lowered his head to take her mouth.

5

Jake's kiss was charged with the elemental need, the primitive hunger Sabrina had sensed in him that morning in Portland. Dear God! Had it only been that morning that she had lain like this in his arms?

No, not like this. Tonight was different and far more dangerous. Tonight her body and her mind were crying out with a compassion that was evolving into passion. She could not understand how the borders between the two had blurred so quickly, but she was rapidly becoming trapped in the force of her own escalating desire.

Jake's lips moved on hers with slow, deliberate sensuality. It was as if he were drinking from the well of her passion, trying to draw forth greater and greater quantities. When her mouth softened and flowered beneath his, he groaned heavily and lowered his weight to cover her completely.

Sabrina felt crushed into the thick pad of the chaise

longue, vividly aware of a host of sensations all at once: the surge of his tongue into the deepest recesses of her mouth, the heavy weight of his body on hers, the feel of his hands as he brought them to her shoulders and held her firmly beneath him.

"Sabrina! God! How I need you tonight."

She moaned his name softly. When had a man ever needed her? Really needed her? Her father hadn't needed or wanted the responsibility of a daughter. Her husband had only wanted to use her to achieve his own ends. The men she encountered in her social life seemed to need a woman only as a partner in the sexual games they played. Sabrina had countered those games with a few of her own, never letting a man get too close, never allowing him to win his game. She had learned her lesson, she thought. The vast majority of men simply did not comprehend or wish for genuine commitment or love.

Which was not to say that Jake wanted commitment or love either, she tried to tell herself, feeling dazed and overwhelmed by his fiercely rising passion.

But he most definitely was not playing games, either. Whatever else was happening between them, his need and desire for her were as fundamental and solid tonight as the man himself. The truth of that seemed to radiate from him, enveloping her in heated waves.

Sabrina sank beneath those waves, surrendering to the need within herself that sought to match the need in him.

"Sabrina!" Her name was a husky claim there in the darkness on the balcony and she knew he had sensed the meaning of her softening body. With everything that was male in him Jake was aware of the yielding in her and he reached out to accept the feminine surrender with all of his strength.

His hand went to the sash of the apricot robe, untying

it impatiently, and then the robe was slipped off her shoulders and left to lie beneath her on the pad of the chaise longue. Sabrina was barely aware of the process. His fingers moved over her with such hunger and sensitivity that she could think only of where they would touch her next. When the shoulder straps of the gossamer nightgown were pushed aside to expose her breasts, Sabrina trembled.

As the nightgown was lowered to her waist, Jake tore his mouth from hers to follow the retreating line of apricot nylon. His kisses burned down her throat to her shoulders. She felt his excitingly rough palm on her nipple, sensed the aching tautness it elicited, and her own hands went to his hair, clenching.

"Oh, Jake. Jake, I don't understand," she began on the merest breath of a sigh. "How can you do this to me?" The question was left hanging. Sabrina was unable to summon enough coherence to ask it fully. She wanted an answer, though, wanted to know who and what he was that he could draw forth a range of emotions unlike anything she had ever known. They swirled around her, making her forget all her own rules and caution.

"Trust me, Sabrina," he groaned against her breast. "I'll take care of you. Put yourself in my keeping." His tongue flicked out to circle the budding nipple and Sabrina shivered again.

Who was taking care of whom? The strange question floated through her head and then was gone, lost in the wave of passion. Around them the silvered darkness draped a protective blanket, allowing them privacy even as it seemed to Sabrina she had never felt so free.

The blood raced in her veins and her legs moved in restless invitation beneath the weight of his thighs. Her own impatience should have astounded her but she had only a fleeting chance to acknowledge it. There were too many other demands on her senses.

"Jake?" She looked up at him from beneath heavy lashes as he pulled briefly away from her.

"I'm not going anywhere, butterfly." The edge of his hard mouth lifted in sensual amusement. Then he was lifting the nightgown completely free of her body, tossing it heedlessly onto the tiled floor of the balcony. At the edge of the chaise longue he unclasped the heavy brass buckle of his belt, unzipped his jeans and stepped out of them. He was wearing nothing underneath.

Sabrina drew in her breath at the sight of his aroused body bathed in the timeless light of a tropical moon. Here on the edge of the ocean with the warm breezes caressing their bodies and the muted crash of the surf in the distance, everything seemed fated to be as it was.

Sitting down on the edge of the chaise longue, Jake drew a hand slowly along the length of her body. Her eyes met his with a combination of tenderness and longing and desire. There was a question buried in the depths of that gaze but it was lost in the other, more potent emotions gleaming there, and Jake must have known it.

"I need to make you mine tonight, butterfly," he rasped huskily as he moved his callused fingers across each exquisitely sensitive nipple. "Do you understand, Sabrina? Afterward you'll fly only with me, never away from me."

She realized vaguely that he was seeking some kind of confirmation from her that she understood his meaning, but she didn't. She didn't even want to think about an "afterward." Tonight all she could concentrate on was him.

"I don't want to talk, Jake. Not now." She held out her

arms to him and after the briefest of hesitations Jake
came down to her in a heated rush.

"In the morning," he breathed hoarsely, "in the
morning we'll talk."

"Yes," she agreed, willing to consent to anything
tonight so that he would continue with the beautiful
lovemaking. The desire to know him completely was so
strong in her now that she would probably have agreed
to whatever he said.

He traced a line of heated kisses from the base of her
throat down her breasts and across the gentle curve of
her stomach. His fingers moved on the inside of her knee,
finding a cache of nerve endings there that Sabrina had
never even guessed existed. He did something to them
that reminded her of the way he had touched her elbow
in the airplane. There was no pain, but the sensation
which resulted took away her breath. It left her trembling
and dazed.

Then he began to stroke a path up along her inner
thigh and the gentle assault escalated until Sabrina was a
twisting, arching, pleading creature of energy and light in
his arms. She was distantly aware of the fact that he had
an uncanny knowledge of the most sensitive areas of her
body and that he knew how to manipulate them in a way
she had never known. It was not the skilled technique of
a practiced lover or an experienced seducer. Her husband had been all too well acquainted with such methods
and it had been one of the frustrations of her marriage
that they hadn't worked particularly well on Sabrina. In
her efforts to please she had learned to fake her satisfaction, and Stan Northrup's ego had been such that he had
never guessed.

Tonight everything was different. Everything was for
real. She did not sense the deliberate techniques of the

sophisticated lover. Jake touched her body with another kind of knowledge altogether and he left a trail of fire in his wake. When his fingers found the ultimate point of her passion, Sabrina thought she would go out of her head.

"Now, Jake! Please, now!" This couldn't be her, pleading for a man, but it was. It was.

"Spread your wings for me, butterfly," he growled, his hand prodding apart her thighs. "Spread your wings and let me take you completely."

She obeyed, deliriously caught up in the moment. His sensual imagery made her feel exotic and exquisite and ecstatic. What butterfly would resist capture when the hunter made her feel so incredibly special?

"Hold on to me, sweetheart," Jake whispered as he settled into the warmth between her legs. "This time we'll fly together."

And then he moved against her, thrusting forward to pin her body inescapably beneath his with a force that left her momentarily stunned. As an act of utter possession, it was almost indescribable. Sabrina knew herself claimed, her slenderness made a part of him. She froze beneath the psychological and the physical impact.

Her lashes lifted, her eyes seeking his as he lay still and hard within her. She found him looking down at her, his face only inches from her own. The moonlight played against the starkly etched lines of his face, and the unfathomable depths of his eyes were a timeless primeval sea.

For an eternity they lay utterly still, their eyes locked together as fiercely as their bodies. The messages that passed between them were intense and timeless and, to Sabrina, not completely understood. Then Jake's hands moved to wrap her close, crushing her small breasts with his broad chest, and he began a rhythmic motion that seemed to build a spiraling stairway. Together they climbed the glittering passage, racing upward so rapidly that Sabrina's breath started to come in quick little gasps.

She felt the strange tightness in her lower body and clung violently to the hard contours of Jake's back. Something was happening within her that she didn't quite know how to handle. The only safety lay in hanging on to the man responsible for the intense, tautening sensation. Her nails sank deeply into his skin and the small pain seemed to please him.

"Oh, Jake, please, I don't . . . I can't . . . What will happen?" The words came in broken little shards from her lips as her eyes squeezed tightly shut and her nails dug deeper.

"Fold your wings around me and hold me as close as you can," he grated against the skin of her shoulder. "Hold me, butterfly!"

Mesmerized by their dizzying flight, she did as he said, wrapping her legs around his waist and tightening her arms at his neck. He slid one hand beneath her to the small of her back, briefly playing once again with the nerves there, and then he probed lower with a calculated touch.

"Oh, my God! Jake! *Jake!*" Jake choked off her cry with his mouth.

Everything seemed to burst within her. An unbelievably voluptuous convulsion took her, sending reverberating shivers throughout her entire body. Sabrina lost herself in it, surrendering completely to it and the man who had caused it.

Her reaction sent Jake hurtling over the same ledge. His body arched violently against her and he used the depths of her mouth to stifle his own shout of satisfaction.

It was only as Sabrina tumbled down with him through the mists of the aftermath of their flight that she finally came to her senses enough to realize why Jake had moved to cut off her final cry and his own. Their balcony provided sufficient privacy from curious eyes, but it was only one in a long row and there were similar rows of balconies above and below them. It was a safe bet that nearly all the other guests would be sleeping with their balcony windows open to the evening breezes, and in the darkness there would be plenty of ears to hear what eyes could not see.

Sabrina knew a sense of shock at the knowledge that she had been far past caring about the nearby presence of others. Then she drifted into a nebulous haze, curling instinctively into the warmth of the man who still lay half-sprawled across her.

Jake lifted his head from the curve of her shoulder as the deliciously lazy satisfaction spread through his body. He looked down at the love-gentled face of the woman in his arms, aware of everything about her, from the way her lashes lay along her cheek to the slick feel of her perspiration-damp stomach.

It came to him then that this was the real reason he'd waged the fierce war for mental survival in that Southeast Asian prison. He stared wonderingly down at his compassionate, sensual butterfly and knew that she was going to make the struggle worthwhile. Somehow a part of him must have sensed that this woman was waiting for him.

He shook his head, half-indulgent at his fanciful thoughts, and then he gently shifted his weight to one side, cradling her pliant form close. His hand moved along the curve of her hip in slow, remembered delight. It *had* been like capturing a butterfly. A very passionate, exotic little butterfly who, he realized in pleased amusement, had been quite startled at the depths of her own sensual response.

From now on, Jake told himself, he would be the only man to provide her that elemental pleasure, just as he would be the only man with the right to protect her. She was his, had given herself completely into his keeping even if she didn't fully realize the fact yet.

Jake lay back against the pillow beside her, aware that she was falling asleep. For a time he simply looked at the delicate shape of her in the moonlight, the small, high curve of her breast and the flare of her hip. Her body was made for his hands. Deliberately he covered one nipple with his palm and smiled at the way it reacted, even though Sabrina was nearly fast asleep.

What would she say when she awoke? That thought wiped the trace of a smile from his mouth. There was no sense in fooling himself tonight. She wasn't going to open her eyes in the morning with the realization that her fate was sealed, even though he'd already tried to warn her. There was too much going on in that lively brain of hers, memories of men who couldn't be trusted to abide by lasting commitments, and fears of letting a man get as close as he had gotten tonight. She was a spirited, independent woman and she wasn't likely to appreciate the fact that he had rushed the relationship to this conclusion. She would have preferred a slow, safe courtship if she wanted any courtship at all and she had made it clear that she would be more likely to welcome such a courtship from a nonthreatening male like Dryden.

Jake let out a long, thoughtful sigh as he raised his eyes to stare up into the starry night. No, she wasn't going to be pleased with what had happened tonight, not after she'd had a chance to realize the full extent of the claim he had staked.

He'd worry about it in the morning. Right now he was sleepy. Satiated, satisfied and content. Damn! But it was good to be so drowsy and to know you were going to fall asleep beside a woman who knew how to lead you through the panic to safety.

It was a very different kind of panic that woke Sabrina at dawn the next morning. A wave of very feminine, very ancient panic which combined with the fears that were uniquely hers.

She opened her eyes slowly to the Hawaiian dawn and found herself lying half-trapped under Jake's bare leg. They were both still lying on the wide chaise longue but sometime during the night Jake had apparently retrieved a blanket from the bed. It covered them now, a light veil of protection against the cool morning air.

For a few tense seconds Sabrina lay utterly still, staring out over the ocean, which in the odd morning light seemed the same shade of unfathomable gray as Jake's eyes.

The second morning in a row. Sabrina closed her lashes briefly in dismay. She could hardly believe what had occurred. This was the second morning in a row that she had awakened in Jake's arms. But unlike yesterday morning, when explanations and excuses could be made and when nothing terribly final had happened anyway, this morning was dawning with the feel of disaster about it.

My God! How had she let herself wind up like this? How had she let herself lower all the carefully constructed barriers? And with a man she had known for only two days?

Her mind reeled at the realization of what she had done. Memories of the compassion and concern which had led her out onto the balcony the previous evening came crowding in as if eager to provide her with some faint excuse for what she had allowed to happen. But none of those excuses was going to give her solace. Sabrina knew that much in the depths of her soul.

Because in the end she had stayed with Jake, not out of compassion, but out of passion.

The restless unease swept over her in a violent fashion as that fact registered, and Sabrina found herself sliding carefully out from under Jake's weight. When she was on her feet she hurried away from the balcony, vividly conscious of her nudity. She turned, once inside the room, to cast a stricken, terribly vulnerable glance back at Jake's sleeping form. He was lying sprawled on the lounge, the blanket draped at his waist. The smoothly muscled contours of his chest and shoulders were a solid, bluntly masculine note against the flower-splashed mattress pad.

His lashes were closed and he didn't stir as Sabrina turned and hurried from his room into her own. Jake was asleep, she thought fleetingly as she pulled on a pair of jeans and found a bateau-necked top in vivid stripes of purple and red and yellow. He was *asleep!* Because of her?

Oh, hell! What did that matter? Disgustedly Sabrina slid her feet into a pair of sandals, grabbed her hotel-room key and hurried out into the hall. Without pausing to think about it, she went along the silent corridor until she found the stairs down to the beach.

Her hair was already in disarray, so when a faint breeze off the ocean caught it and played with the tawny tendrils, it didn't make much difference. Sabrina lifted her face to the miracle of an island morning and plunged ahead at a brisk run, heading for the water's edge. There she came to a halt, drew in several deep breaths and then turned to pace furiously on the hard-packed sand.

Hands thrust into the back pockets of her jeans, she walked toward the far end of the beach. Her brows were drawn together in a disgusted scowl and her whole body radiated the tension she was feeling.

What in hell was she going to do now? God only knew what Jake would be thinking when he awoke this morning. No, that wasn't strictly true. Sabrina could make a damn good guess about what he would be thinking!

He would assume that a full-scale affair had been begun out on that balcony last night. He would assume that he was going to have the benefit of a sleeping companion for the duration of his job as bodyguard.

Some bodyguard! She had been right when she had caustically wondered who was going to protect her from the man assigned to protect her. Just look at what had happened! Sabrina's teeth sank into her lower lip as she recalled the events of the evening. How could she have been so incredibly stupid?

"If you stay out here on this balcony a moment longer, I'm going to take you," he'd told her in the bluntest of warnings. And she'd stayed. God help her, but she'd *stayed!* No matter what she told herself, there was no getting around the fact that she had stayed with him after he'd given her a chance to return to her own room. Being a man, Sabrina thought furiously, Jake was going to remember that little detail very clearly.

"Dammit to *hell!*" she hissed aloud, kicking wretchedly at a broken shell. "What am I going to do now?"

First things first. She had to get control of herself before she would be able to get control of the situation. One night of passion in a near-stranger's arms didn't make her suddenly vulnerable to that stranger. She was made of stronger stuff than that, surely! Hadn't she learned anything at all about men in her lifetime?

They could be amusing, pleasant company, even interesting. But they were not to be trusted when it came to making commitments. That was the one bare fact that must always be remembered.

And last night, Sabrina reminded herself, Jake hadn't even pretended to be making a commitment. There hadn't even been superficial words to make it all seem okay at the time. Sabrina shook her head once in utter bewilderment. She had never expected to be so easily seduced by a man, but if she had thought about it she would have assumed that if such an event were to occur, it would be well camouflaged in words of love and lasting commitment. Soft, romantic words; words of promise.

Well, in that respect, she told herself grimly, Jake hadn't lied. But then, he hadn't needed to resort to lying. She had been his for the taking.

"Damn, damn, damn!"

Enraged with herself, Sabrina sank down onto a rock, one of many that extended from an outcropping at the far end of the beach. Automatically her disconsolate gaze roved back along the water's edge toward the magnificent hotel which gleamed in the bright morning light.

Jake was coming toward her along the beach.

For a shocked instant her stricken eyes locked with his, and then Sabrina resolutely swung her focus back out to sea. She was not going to be vulnerable to this man. She would not again be vulnerable to *any* man! Yet there was no denying that the sight of him pacing toward her across the sand, his hard face set in implacable lines, gray eyes totally unreadable, sent a rush of awareness through her. His brown hair was lightly tossed in the gentle breeze and the faded jeans he wore seemed molded to the strong thighs her body remembered so well.

He had his hands shoved into his front pockets and there was an aggressive, determined aura about him as he came to a halt beside her, feet slightly spread apart. Sabrina's already tense frame seemed to be strung as taut as a bowstring as she defiantly refused to look up at him.

It was Jake who spoke first, and if there had been no words of commitment or enduring promise in that soft, gritty voice last night, there certainly wasn't anything gentle or reassuring about his conversation this morning, either.

"Sabrina, don't ever, *ever* do that again."

The command carried enough power to break her steadfast attention on the horizon. Uncomprehendingly she glanced up at him. Whatever she had expected him to say this morning, that wasn't quite it.

"Don't do what again?" she asked in a distant tone. Don't ever sleep with him again?

He didn't move. "Don't ever run off by yourself the way you did this morning. You're not to go anywhere out of my sight, and you know it. My job, as I am obliged to keep reminding you, is to protect you. Remember?"

She surged to her feet, incensed. How dare he make this the first topic on the agenda after what had happened between them? How *dare* he? Who the hell did Jake Devlin think he was? "Don't worry, Jake," she snapped, her hands curling into small fists, "I remember very clearly what you were hired to do, and your job description did not include seducing me! Or did you think it would be easier to keep track of me if I were under your control in that way? Did you think I'd wake up this morning so entranced with your lovemaking that I'd willingly obey you for the duration of this farce?"

His cool gray eyes became hooded and dangerous. "Sabrina, listen to me."

"I listened to you last night, and look where it got me! But it's not going to make any difference, Jake, do you understand? What happened last night could have happened between any two people caught up in a situation like ours. Look at this," she ordered tightly, waving a hand to encompass the whole island. "Here we are on a tropical island in a hotel suite with a connecting door. I suppose something was bound to happen!"

"It was?" There was a quizzical gleam in the depths of that cool gaze now.

"Well, maybe not if I'd had a bodyguard who didn't get up in the middle of the night and open the connecting door!" she hissed back.

"I wanted to look at you," he explained simply. "I'm more comfortable when I can see you. Especially at night."

"That's a ridiculous reason!"

"You didn't have to come out onto the balcony looking for me," he pointed out gently. "And you didn't have to stay, once you found me. Why did you stay, Sabrina?"

"Why did I stay?" she repeated, infuriated. "I stayed because I thought it might help you get to sleep if you talked about your nighttime claustrophobia. I only came out onto that balcony to talk, dammit!"

"And after we'd finished talking?" he prompted in a voice of torn velvet. "Why did you stay then? Was it out of pity, Sabrina? Were you feeling so sorry for me that you decided to sleep with me as a way of extending comfort and sympathy?"

She flinched, recoiling a step. What was he talking about now? "Comfort? Pity? Are you out of your mind, Jake?" she demanded, rushing heedlessly into her next words before stopping to think. "I'm not stupid enough to sleep with a man out of pity! For God's sake, it's myself I should be pitying, not you! You can take care of yourself, can't you? You survived all those months in that horrid prison, you're an expert in some exotic field of self-defense, you take on bodyguarding jobs to pick up a little spare cash and you use those sneaky martial-arts techniques to seduce a woman so that she can't even think straight! No, dammit, I don't feel sorry for you. I'd like to wrap my fingers around your throat and throttle you! I'd like to slap your face! I'd like to be a martial-arts expert who was good enough to beat you! That's what I'd like to do!"

"I see," he said very carefully. But all the care in the world couldn't hide the faint, telltale relaxation of the tightly drawn lines around his mouth and eyes. Nor could it disguise the flicker of relief which came and went in those gray depths.

Sabrina saw all of that and was horrified that she'd been such a fool as to miss the one golden opportunity that had been handed to her that morning. She almost gritted her teeth as she stared up at him and acknowledged to herself that she'd blithely ignored the one weapon that had been at her fingertips.

She ought to have claimed refuge in the excuse he had offered her. She should have agreed wholeheartedly that it was compassion and pity which had made her stay in his arms last night. Such an excuse would have freed her from so many of the pitfalls which lay ahead now.

"It's too late, Sabrina," Jake pointed out almost sympathetically as she stood in front of him, berating herself. He must have known exactly what was going through her mind. "You've already admitted that you stayed with me for some reason other than pity. You can't change your mind now and claim differently." And then he smiled. One of his rare, engaging smiles that caught at her heart. "Thanks, Sabrina. That was the one thing that would have been hard to take this morning."

"The thought that it was pity that caused me to make such a fool of myself?" she shot back roundly, seeking to recover some lost ground. "Well, don't get too arrogant at the thought of being able to seduce me so easily! It won't happen again, Jake. I'm only human and I've got needs just like everyone else, but last night was a fluke. I have no interest in short-term relationships with men I hardly know. What happened last night does not automatically elevate you to the status of lover as well as bodyguard, Jake Devlin. I suppose I'd had too much to drink and it was late at night on a tropical island and I was with a man who seems to have learned a lot about the female body in the course of studying his martial-arts techniques. *But it won't happen again!*"

He put out his hands and grasped her shoulders, gently holding her still in front of him. "Sabrina, Sabrina," he murmured, his mouth crooking slightly at one corner. "The only excuse that might have stood a ghost of a chance of working for a short while was the one you threw away, the one involving pity. All those others aren't going to hold water, and you know it. Not even the one about having needs like everyone else. You didn't use me to satisfy those needs, did you? Up until last night I'm not sure you even knew how much passion there was in you to be satisfied!"

"Why, you arrogant, chauvinistic, high-handed *bodyguard!*" she gasped, appalled at the extent of his perception. Had she been so shockingly obvious in her reactions?

Jake shook his head once, the faint smile disappearing. "Sweetheart, don't be afraid of me."

"I'm not afraid of you," Sabrina declared royally. She stepped out from under his hands and he let her go. "I just want to make sure you're not expecting last night to evolve into a pleasant little two-week interlude for you. How many times do I have to explain to you that you work for me, Jake Devlin? The events of last night were a mistake on both our parts!"

"You mean it was a mistake on your part because you

should have kept me in line instead of letting me make love to you?" he growled.

"Precisely! But I try to learn from my mistakes," she assured him arrogantly, turning to stride back up the beach toward the hotel. "And I won't repeat the one I made last night."

"And I also trust you won't repeat the one you made this morning," he drawled, following grimly at her heels.

"What are you talking about?" She slanted him a disgruntled glance.

"The way you skipped off without telling me where you were going."

"For heaven's sake! I've had a mortifying, infuriating, traumatic experience and you have the nerve to complain because I went off by myself to think for a while?" she choked out.

"As you keep reminding me, I work for you," he retorted a little too smoothly. "Keeping an eye on you is fundamental to the job, I'm afraid."

"Of all the . . . !" Sabrina broke off, unable to find sufficient words. "Forget it. How could I possibly expect a man to understand what I'm going through?" she muttered half under her breath. "You'd better hurry, Jake. We're going to breakfast and then on to the first seminar. Would you care to have an itemized agenda so you'll know exactly where to find me at any given time?" she added sweetly.

"That won't be necessary," he stated calmly, "since I'll be right there beside you all along."

6

~~~~~~~~~~~~~~~~~~

He was right there beside her, all right.

Sabrina didn't even try to ignore him at breakfast, nor did she try to put some distance between them in the classroom that had been set up in one of the hotel meeting rooms. It would have been pointless, she told herself ruefully. There was no way to get rid of the man. All she could do was learn to tolerate his presence and make damn certain she didn't get herself into the precarious, highly charged situation in which she had found herself the previous evening. She was on her guard now, Sabrina decided vengefully as he sank down beside her in the seminar room. She had not spent all this time building her protective walls only to have them ripped asunder by the lure of a man like Jake Devlin.

The sixty or so people attending the seminar soon filed in and filled the room. A lecture podium had been placed at the front, together with the usual audiovisual paraphernalia, and there was an air of expectation among the medieval devotees. Across the room Perry Dryden caught Sabrina's eye and smiled hopefully. She returned the look with more than her usual amount of friendly warmth. Perry appeared so nice this morning. There was nothing overwhelming or dangerous or arrogant about him. She smiled again and could have sworn he blushed.

"Don't," Jake murmured beside her, breaking in on her speculation about the cause of the faint red stain on Perry's features.

"Don't what?"

"Don't encourage Dryden. You'll only be getting both of you into more trouble than either of you can handle."

"As long as we're listing dos and don'ts, I'll give you one to keep in mind," Sabrina shot back just as Larissa Waverly swept dramatically into the room to take her place at the podium. "Don't threaten me!"

There was no opportunity for Jake to respond to that because Dr. Waverly proved herself an expert at taking hold of an audience. It wasn't just that she was a very striking woman or that she made the most of her physical assets that morning by wearing a sheer, low-cut sundress, but the fact that she knew and loved her subject. That crucial message dominated the morning seminar, and Sabrina, along with everyone else in the room, was soon caught up in the intricacies of the Age of Chivalry.

"What lends real magic to this era is not the tales of heroic battles and knight-errantry," Larissa Waverly pointed out during her talk. "Keep in mind that such legends of valor and strength have come down to us from countless other ages and a variety of nations. By themselves the heroic quests of the Knights of the Round Table would be no different from other such tales of their kind.

No, what makes this knightly culture of the Middle Ages unique is the way the literature and the songs of the age introduced the concept of courtly love.

"This new element of romance was largely a product of the troubadours of southern France, who composed songs and poetry for the rather limited world of the knights and lords and ladies of the castles. You must remember that marriage was almost entirely a business matter in those days. Acquiring lands and ensuring heirs for those acquisitions required that marriages be arranged in a realistic fashion. Most men and women of the time accepted that. They were as capable of being practical about business as people of any other era.

"But the concept of a courtly romance, a love from afar which inspired and ennobled, was a delightful concept for all concerned. It took hold of the imagination of the knightly classes almost at once, and it changed forever our concept of men in shining armor."

Sabrina felt her arm gently nudged, and Jake leaned toward her to comment in a whisper, "It didn't particularly change that concept for the better, if you ask me."

"No one did!" she shot back as quietly as possible. She was aware of his slight shrug.

At the podium Dr. Waverly went cheerfully along with her lecture. "Many times in the Arthurian romances we see examples of the extremes to which a knight would go in order to please the lady he idolized. There is a tale of Sir Gawain, for example, deliberately making a fool and an apparent coward of himself at an important tournament because he had been bidden by a lady to do so. He is supposed to have willingly endured the scorn and laughter of his fellow knights and the noble audience just so that the lady's whim was satisfied."

At that moment Perry Dryden raised his hand. "Such

an incident takes place in one of the stories concerning Lancelot," he remarked a bit timidly.

"Indeed it does." Dr. Waverly smiled approvingly. "Lancelot was incognito at one particular tournament but he was winning every event in sight. Guenevere suspected his real identity, and to test her theory, sent a message to him that he was to start losing. He promptly obeyed. His lady's wishes were more important than anything else, including his honor and reputation as a fighter."

Again Jake leaned surreptitiously toward Sabrina. "The thing to do with ladies like the ones Gawain and Lancelot were trying to please is to beat them," he advised dryly.

A totally unexpected surge of amusement rose in Sabrina as it struck her just how ludicrous the extremes of chivalry probably sounded to a man like Jake Devlin. "Lucky for you, you were born into a more modern age, isn't it?" she tried to retort quellingly.

"Oh, I don't know," he murmured laconically. "I get the feeling modern women can be just as difficult and whimsical."

Before she could think of anything to say to that, another voice was interrupting Larissa Waverly's lecture. "It's true enough that such events were common in the legends, Dr. Waverly," commented a balding man in a brightly colored aloha shirt, "but how did those legends affect the people who listened to them?"

"You must remember that the Arthurian legends were one of the principal means of educating a real-life knight," Larissa said easily. "It was from those tales of chivalry that a real knight of the Middle Ages derived his sense of identity, of being superior to other classes. It gave him a romantic illusion which made his world seem somehow elegant and wonderful. And there are instances of genuine knights going out of their way to honor a chosen lady. Ulrich von Liechtenstein, for example, who lived around 1250, is famous for some of the exploits which he undertook to please his lady. On one occasion he learned that his lady was surprised to hear he still had a finger which she believed had been lost in one of the many tournaments he'd fought. Without hesitation he cut off the finger and had it sent to her!"

Jake moved restlessly beside Sabrina. "I think I'm going to be sick," he announced disgustedly.

"Hush!" she whispered urgently. But it was too late. This time Larissa Waverly heard the low-voiced comment and her vivid green eyes turned invitingly toward Jake. "Yes, Mr. Devlin? Did you have something to add to the discussion?"

"Oh, my God!" Sabrina groaned under her breath. There was nothing she could do, however. Jake would have to handle this one himself.

He didn't hesitate. "It seems to me, Dr. Waverly, that while the Arthurian legends no doubt served as a source of entertainment and amusement and even education during the Middle Ages, human nature being what it is, especially the nature of men who make their living with their swords, I doubt that there were very many von Liechtensteins running around. He was probably just an early, eccentric Arthurian enthusiast. If you want my opinion, most knights probably used the tales and legends to pretty up their warfare and to help them justify the grabbing of other people's property. It gave them a way to do that sort of thing with honor and renown. Not a bad deal if you can get away with it. What man wouldn't just as soon be painted as an epic hero when he reaches out and takes what he wants by force? I expect most of them knew damn well what they were doing!"

It was too much for Sabrina. Without waiting to be recognized by the professor, she turned on Jake, speaking loudly enough so that the whole class could hear. "Mr. Devlin has an extremely narrow view of the concept of chivalry," she declared grimly, her eyes clashing with his. "He is a very practical man, you see. If a male wants something and it's in his power to take it, why shouldn't he? And his views apply to women as well as property, don't they, Mr. Devlin? Why don't you give the class the benefit of your opinion on chivalric love?"

She realized belatedly that they were the cynosure of all eyes now. In her tense, high-strung state she had allowed her tongue to run away with her in front of sixty people. Appalled, she continued to stare at Jake.

"Yes, Mr. Devlin," Larissa interjected with apparent interest. "Why don't you give us your opinion on the concept of chivalric love?"

Jake's eyes never left Sabrina's glaring gaze. "Practically speaking, Dr. Waverly, I don't believe it exists and I'd be willing to bet that most of the knights of the Middle Ages didn't fall victim to the concept either, except as an amusing illusion. If a man truly loves a woman, he's going to want to reach out and take her. Men can feel a number of emotions toward a woman to whom they are attracted. They might need her or use her or love her or want to please her, but if they're heavily involved with her one way or another, they're going to want to sleep with her. Just as Lancelot eventually wound up sleeping with Guenevere. I suspect most real-life knights were quite aware of the fundamentals of human nature. It's only in the legends that supposedly wise kings like Arthur display such an unrealistic grasp of human nature. I sure as hell wouldn't have let that sneaky Lancelot within a hundred feet of my queen's bedchamber!"

There was no chance for an enraged Sabrina to make a rebuttal. The classroom seemed to explode with sixty voices, each trying to express an opinion. It was the perfect example of a classroom discussion that has ignited and taken off under its own power. Larissa Waverly smiled benignly from her position at the podium and began to guide and moderate the chaos of comments. Nothing was as satisfying to a truly professional instructor as having the students really sink their teeth into the subject at hand. Dr. Waverly was nothing if not a true professional. She couldn't have been more pleased.

Three hours later, at noon, when class ended for the day, Sabrina sailed out of the meeting room, heading toward the hotel dining room for lunch. Jake followed doggedly at her heels as usual. When they sat down at a small table near the window, Sabrina eyed him speculatively across the short distance, her toe tapping in ill-concealed irritation. He returned her look with a totally bland one of his own.

The staring contest lasted for about sixty seconds and then Sabrina's sense of humor got the better of her. "You do have a way of livening up a classroom discussion," she allowed.

His expression changed, becoming more readable, and what she read there was a sense of the ridiculous that almost matched her own. "You provoked me," he accused.

"It's all my fault?"

"Definitely. Are you going to have the teriyaki sandwich or the pineapple-and-papaya salad?"

"I was thinking about having your head served up on a platter!"

He grinned suddenly, devastatingly. "Poor Sabrina. I really haven't turned out to be at all as you expected a bodyguard to be, have I?"

"No," she told him firmly, picking up her menu. "But I think I can still find some use for you."

He arched an eyebrow. "I'm flattered."

"You won't be when you find out how I plan to put you to use."

She showed him after lunch, loading him up with a beach umbrella from the hotel beach stand, several towels, sunscreen lotion and books on medieval culture. Then she led him down to the beach. Privately she gave Jake credit for not complaining about the load, and when she had chosen a location with due deliberation, he obediently put the umbrella into position and arranged the towels.

"There's something I don't understand here," he said meekly as he surveyed his handiwork. "Why are we sitting under an umbrella and using total sun-block lotion? Don't you want a tan?"

"The sun's bad for you. Tanning is no longer considered healthy," Sabrina informed him as she began unfastening the large wooden buttons on her swimsuit cover-up. "I saw an article on the subject in one of the medical magazines the library gets." Another item of miscellaneous information, she thought wryly. She seemed to be devoting her life to acquiring an extensive collection of miscellaneous knowledge. What would interest her next, after this seminar on chivalry?

Jake watched her as she slipped off the brightly striped top. "You're going to spend ten days in Hawaii and try not to get a tan? Perhaps you should have chosen another vacation spot!"

"I like the beach." She shrugged as the cover-up came off completely, exposing a revealing brilliant yellow bikini.

Jake's gray gaze swept over the small scraps of material molding her slender figure. "Good God, Sabrina.

Some man is going to have to take your wardrobe in hand one of these days. For a woman who claims she doesn't want a tan, you're sure dressed to get a good one! Is that the best you could do by way of a swimsuit?"

"Sometimes I get the impression you're rather conservative in your taste," she drawled, leaning back against a beach pillow and picking up one of the books. A part of her was perversely pleased at having offended his sense of decorum. She realized vaguely that she felt like offending Jake at every turn today. It was little enough recompense for what he'd done to her last night, and he deserved it.

"Let's just say I prefer my clients not to make spectacles of themselves," he retorted, unfastening his jeans and stepping out of them. Underneath he wore a modest pair of swim trunks which, by their very lack of emphasis, seemed to draw attention to the confident strength in his lean frame. Sabrina realized belatedly that she was staring at him as he undressed and hastily turned her attention back to her book.

"I feel the same way about the people who work for me," she told him smoothly. "I'd just as soon you didn't make a spectacle of yourself, either. And to prevent another incident such as that which took place this morning in class, I am going to drill you on some fundamental facts about the concept of chivalry."

Jake reclined on his back beside her, propping himself up on his elbows so that he could scan the beach scene in front of him. She sensed the sudden seriousness in him, and something inside Sabrina went on the alert.

"Before we get to the lesson of the day," Jake said coolly, "I think we should talk about last night. Now that you've had a chance to calm down—"

The fragile truce which had been constructed during the morning was shattered as far as Sabrina was concerned. "I don't want to talk about it, Jake. It was a mistake and I do not intend to let it happen again."

"And if it does?"

"If I thought there was a genuine danger of such a thing occurring again, I would be in the market for a new bodyguard," she grated fiercely, trying to focus on the text in front of her. "But it's not going to happen again, is it, Jake? We're two adults and now that we're on guard we won't be letting our emotions run away with us a second time!"

He turned his head to look at her. Sabrina saw the elemental promise in the gray pools of his eyes and shivered. For a moment she went very still, feeling like a small, trapped creature. A butterfly? Was that what he had called her? Instantly she rejected the image of beauty and helplessness that the word conjured.

"No, Jake," she heard herself whisper even though he had said nothing. "No!"

Whatever Jake might have replied died on his lips as a small boy materialized beside the umbrella, a red plastic pail and shovel in one hand and an expression of hopeful curiosity on his rounded features.

"Want to help me build a castle?" the child inquired politely of Jake, clearly dismissing Sabrina as a viable candidate for such construction. "I asked everyone else but they're all too busy." He waved the shovel to indicate almost everyone else on the beach.

Jake regarded the youngster gravely. "A castle, hmmm? Funny you should mention a castle. Do you know anything about Arthurian romances or chivalric love or knight-errantry?"

The boy thought about it for a moment, small brow furrowing before he answered. "Nope."

Jake was on his feet in a lithe movement, grinning down at the would-be castle builder. "In that case I will be happy to help you build a sand castle. The only thing is, we have to build it nearby. I have to keep an eye on this lady here,'' he explained apologetically.

The boy glanced at Sabrina and dismissed her as a problem. "Okay. Suits me." He started off toward a stretch of sand that was more firmly packed than the portion on which Sabrina was lying, and Jake went with him.

Sabrina watched them go, half-amused, half-intrigued at the sight of the youngster going off so trustingly with his new friend. She remembered Jake's rapport with the children in his self-defense class. A strange man. When he settled down into the sand beside the boy and began scooping up the material for castle walls, she smiled to herself and went back to her book.

The next time she glanced up, it was to see Jake surrounded by nearly every kid on the beach. Sabrina stared in astonishment at the huge fortification being constructed. Jake was directing operations and no one seemed to be getting in anyone else's way. The construction crew each had a section of the job and the building was flowing smoothly along. A large moat surrounded a fantasy castle composed of an architectural mishmash of spires and turrets and parapets. The builders scurried to and fro, hauling vast quantities of sand and pausing occasionally to consult with the construction supervisor, Jake. Adults passing by began pausing for longer and longer observation. At the rate it was going, the sand castle was going to dominate the beach, Sabrina thought with inner laughter.

The laughter was still in her eyes as Jake glanced up and saw her watching. He responded with a rueful shrug, clearly helpless to stop what he had started; then he went back to work. Sabrina continued to watch in growing fascination. He really was terrific with kids, she thought wonderingly. Was that why he had chosen to teach them instead of adults? So few people had that kind of immediate rapport with children. And he combined it with an inherent discipline that the youngsters seemed to respond to willingly.

There were no tantrums being thrown, no undue squabbling, little unrest among the members of the construction crew. Jake's guidance was eagerly sought and cheerfully followed. And the castle continued to grow.

It was only when adults paused to chat with Jake about the immense fortification taking shape that Sabrina saw the marked difference in the way he dealt with them. Jake was polite and easygoing but there was a careful, remote distance between him and casual passersby that disappeared when one of the kids tugged at his hand to get his attention. Sabrina remembered how she had observed that same shift in him when she had first seen him dealing with the parents of his students. It was as if Jake had built his own personal castle complete with a moat and a drawbridge that could be lowered or drawn up at will.

Sabrina thought about that and then drew in a long, shaky breath as a gripping realization flashed into her mind. When Jake was with her, he was often as open as he was with the kids. Since that first night when she had fixed him the hot milk and turned on the television to soothe his "nightmares," he had begun lowering the drawbridge to allow her inside the castle walls.

And last night he had let down the bridge completely, allowing her to invade the vulnerable area behind the fortified barriers.

The problem, Sabrina thought, was that once she was

inside, he had tried to chain her there. Jake had wanted to push past her own personal barriers just as he had allowed her through his.

Sabrina's fingers folded into small fists as she recognized her early-morning panic for exactly what it had been: the fear that Jake had succeeded in his goal. She *had* felt claimed. Claimed, taken, possessed.

But even as she rebelled at the thought of opening herself to a man, she recalled the way he had exposed the vulnerability in himself. It was so hard to think of this man as being vulnerable in any way, and yet she had seen the depths of his private fears last night. She had felt a womanly satisfaction in soothing those fears.

Was that the reason she hadn't fled the hotel and Jake and Hawaii altogether this morning? She had been angry at her own stupid behavior, but her distrust of Jake had not been sufficient to make her book a flight back to the mainland. Instead she had taken him with her to breakfast and on to class and then to the beach. For God's sake, what was she thinking of to treat this man with such a degree of casual arrogance?

It was the vulnerability in him that had done it. It had been her downfall and it was the reason she was feeling so ambivalent today. With any other man she would have been too much on her guard to have allowed the lovemaking to occur.

Men always seemed shallow and superficial to her these days. She no longer trusted them and had little difficulty resisting them. Yet she had found herself in bed with Jake Devlin even though she had known him for less than two days.

She had been seduced by the knowledge that Jake was neither shallow nor superficial but a complex human being with inner fears far more terrifying than her own. He had taken the risk of exposing those fears to her. It was the memory of the way he had allowed her to witness his own vulnerability which held her here today, when, by all rights, she should have been putting as much distance as possible between herself and this very dangerous man.

There was danger and there was danger, she thought with a sigh, leaning back against the beach pillow and picking up the textbook. And there was a wider variety of lures that could be dangled by the male of the species than she would ever have dreamed. The recollection of her own passion, a passion generated by Jake, was a perfect example. Who would have guessed . . . ?

"Excuse me, but I thought you might be getting a little warm out here. I've brought you a piña colada from the beach bar. If you'd like it, that is," Perry Dryden amended hastily as Sabrina glanced up in surprise.

She blinked and then smiled in genuine appreciation. "Why, thank you, Perry. It sounds lovely." Reaching up, she took the chilled glass from his hand and wasn't terribly startled when Perry took the acceptance of his gift as an invitation. He dropped down beside her, his pleasant features composed in a shy, eager-to-please expression. He was wearing dark glasses today instead of his horn-rimmed ones, and Sabrina idly wondered if the sunglasses were prescription. The lenses weren't very thick.

"This is the first time I've seen you alone since we arrived," he observed delicately. Then he removed the dark glasses and glanced meaningfully toward the towering edifice being constructed on the beach.

When Sabrina followed his glance, she realized Jake was watching them, a forbidding expression on his face. She wondered how he had been alerted to Perry's appearance so quickly. The man must have a sixth sense, she decided. Maybe that was a prerequisite for being a successful bodyguard/martial-arts expert. She bent her head and sipped at the piña colada, ignoring Perry's implied question. She realized she didn't want to discuss Jake with him.

"How did you enjoy the class this morning?" she asked instead. "Dr. Waverly is really very good, isn't she?"

"Tops. But is your friend Jake a genuine Arthurian enthusiast? He seemed rather down on the whole notion of chivalry today," Perry observed.

"He is somewhat opinionated on the subject," she agreed lightly, her gaze on Jake again. He hadn't left his construction crew but she knew he was watching her out of the corner of his eye.

"A friend of the family, you said?"

"Something like that." Who could possibly explain the presence of a bodyguard? Better to get off the subject entirely. "Tell me, what do you think of Dr. Waverly's comments on the strong moral streak that's supposed to be a part of courtly love?" Besides, Jake was far too personal a subject!

Like any well-bred courtier, Perry accepted the change in conversation gracefully and they fell into a casual discussion of the morning's seminar. Sabrina was halfway through her piña colada when Jake pronounced the castle finished and took his leave of the construction gang. Then he turned and paced back across the sand toward the umbrella.

Perry Dryden scrambled to his feet at once, as if the other man's approach was the signal for his own dismissal. "It's been nice chatting with you, Sabrina," he murmured, shoving his dark glasses back on his nose with a nervous little gesture. "I'll, uh, see you in class tomorrow morning."

She smiled benignly. "Thanks again for the drink,

Perry. It was very thoughtful of you." Then she watched wryly as he hastened away before Jake reached the umbrella.

"I think you scare him," she complained as Jake lowered himself to the towel beside her.

"Good. What did he want, Sabrina?" His gaze was on the retreating figure of the other man.

"We talked about the class discussion this morning and the topic for tomorrow." She shrugged, slurping the last of the piña colada through the straw. "And he brought me something to drink."

"So I see. Were you thirsty?" He flicked her a lazy glance.

"No, but it was a nice gesture, wasn't it?"

He tilted his head to one side, studying her, and then he started to smile. "Sabrina, my love, if you're trying to make me jealous, you needn't waste your time."

"It wouldn't work?" she challenged, surprised at how annoyed she felt.

"I meant it would be a waste of your time because I already am quite jealous," he explained politely.

"You are?" Her eyes widened at the frank admission.

He leaned back on one elbow, facing her. "As hell. I'm in a difficult position, you see. Dryden's shorter, younger and not as strong as I am. If I beat him to a pulp I'll come out looking like the villain of the piece."

"You certainly would!"

"Don't look so horrified. I won't slaughter Dryden unless you give me cause."

"Jake! What are you saying?" she squeaked, shocked.

"I'm saying that if you want to avoid potential bloodshed, you'll steer clear of the man," Jake retorted steadily, gray eyes suddenly very cool. "If he gets hurt, it will be your fault."

"Of all the outrageous things to say! How dare you

threaten me?" Sabrina jackknifed to a sitting position, glaring at him. "You have no right to use a threat like that to make sure I walk the line you want me to walk!"

But Jake was grinning at her with that engaging, open smile that she knew now was reserved for her and children. He paid no attention at all to the infuriated look on her face, surging easily to his feet and bending down to scoop her up in his arms.

"I think it's time you took a dip. Your temper is not improving in this heat."

"Jake, put me down this instant!"

He did, but not quite that instant. It took him a couple of minutes to wade into the warm sea and lower her gently into the blissful water. Sabrina, who had been far too conscious of his sun-heated skin as he held her against his chest, decided to take his advice and cool herself down in more ways than one. As soon as he released her, she began swimming industriously.

She had gone about fifteen yards down the shore when she realized she wasn't going to lose him that way. He swam beside her almost lazily, exerting barely any effort at all as far as she could tell. When she gave up and let her feet drift down to the sandy bottom, he smiled at her and halted. Then he reached out and cupped her frowning upturned face in his hands, somewhat as she had framed his hard features the night before.

"I'm jealous but I'm not really worried, Sabrina," he confided with gruff gentleness. "Do you know why?"

She went very still in the water, suddenly uncertain and aware once more of her own vulnerability to this man. Wordlessly she waited, feeling trapped.

"I'm not really worried about Dryden because I think that, unlike Guenevere, you wouldn't betray me with another man. You're upset about what happened last night, but you belong to me now and I think you know it."

"Jake, no—!"

He leaned down to claim her parted lips, his own wet and salty on her mouth. His hands slid sleekly down the length of her throat and over the curve of her shoulders as the water lapped at her breasts.

Sabrina shivered, longing to lash out at him and tell him that she didn't need or want his trust, that she owed him no loyalty. But the essence of his warmth and controlled passion captivated her. His hands moved lower, down her back, and before she knew what he was about, the top of the yellow bikini floated free, still suspended from her neck but no longer covering her breasts.

"Jake!"

"Hush," he ordered softly. "I'm between you and the shore and there's no one around us. Nobody can see you, butterfly. Only me. And I need to see by daylight what I've only seen by moonlight. I've been thinking about the passion in you all day, sweetheart."

She tried to move backward, her hazel eyes wide and wary, but he lightly pulled her hands away from her breasts and raised his head to look down at her. The sea rose and fell in soft little swells, alternately revealing and concealing her hardening nipples. Gently but firmly Jake held her wrists to either side of her body and his gray eyes darkened as he absorbed the sight of her.

Sabrina felt breathless, unable to summon up words of protest or even to struggle. Just as she had the night before, she felt bound by the gathering force of Jake's undisguised desire. It sought to ignite her own, and therein lay the real danger. But she couldn't resist.

When he released her wrists and used his thumbs to

graze the tips of her breasts, she moaned softly and collapsed against his chest.

"Sweetheart, don't be afraid of me," he murmured into her tangled wet hair. "Trust me."

"Jake," she managed haltingly, "I don't want an affair. I don't want to get involved!"

"You already are involved. You've invaded my life and made me your protector. We're stuck with each other, remember?"

She heard the gentle humor in him and started to pull away. Almost at once he refastened the clip of the bikini bra. Helplessly she looked up at him, unable to think of all the logical reasons she should have been using to free herself of Jake Devlin. The edge of his mouth curved in subtle, passionate amusement as he assessed the play of emotions on her face. "Come on, butterfly. You look confused enough for one day. Let's go back to shore."

"Jake?" Tremulously Sabrina managed to dig out the necessary words. "Jake, I don't want you to think . . . I mean, just because of that kiss, don't get the idea I'm going to . . ."

"To sleep with me tonight?" he concluded helpfully as he waded out of the sea beside her. "Don't worry, sweetheart. I'll give you a little time if that's really what you want. Now that I know you're mine, I can afford to wait until the right moment."

"What's that supposed to mean?" she flashed, abruptly incensed by his self-assurance.

He looked down at her. "It means I'm very good at waiting until the right moment. I spent six months learning patience the hard way, remember? Go ahead and flutter your wings a bit more, sweetheart, if it makes you feel any better. The truth is, as of last night you're already in my net."

7

~~~~~~~~~~~~~~~~

It was Sabrina who had trouble sleeping that night. She lay in bed, shifting restlessly every ten minutes or so as she searched for a comfortable position. What made settling down to sleep so difficult, she told herself resentfully, was that every time she turned even a few inches, her eyes went to the open connecting door between her room and Jake's.

The door wasn't completely open, only ajar. Sabrina couldn't see around the edge but there was no light on in the other room. Was Jake asleep?

"You turkey!" she scolded herself in a near-silent mutter. "What are you thinking of doing? Getting yourself into the same kind of trouble you got yourself into last night? That man can take care of himself!"

Flopping backward on the pillow in disgust, she reran the strange day she had spent in Jake's company. He had been attentive, polite, always around.

Waiting.

Jake Devlin knew a lot about waiting. He'd staked his claim and now he was prepared to wait for her acceptance of it. A tremor of intuition told Sabrina that when it came to this kind of dangerous contest Jake's patience and nerves were probably a lot better equipped to handle the struggle than her own. Was he really so confident of the outcome?

He hadn't sulked or accused her of teasing him with sex and then withdrawing her favors. He hadn't done any of the things she would have expected a man to do under the circumstances. There was a solid, implacable sureness about him. And that waiting quality.

The moonlight inched slowly across the bed, and through the open window the lulling sound of the surf came with pleasant, soothing monotony. Why wasn't she asleep?

Jake had danced with her in the lounge after dinner that evening but there had been no deliberate seduction on the dance floor. Of course, Sabrina reminded herself with a wry twist of her mouth, the incredibly smooth, gliding coordination he brought to his dancing was a seduction in 'and of itself. But not a deliberate one. He hadn't, for example, used his hands on her sensitive spine the way he had the night before. Nor had he attempted any more purely sensual contact since touching her so intimately that afternoon in the sea. He seemed prepared to keep the promise he had made to her as they'd waded to shore. He'd wait.

Sabrina closed her eyes and found herself listening for the faintest sounds of movement from next door. There were none. *Was* Jake asleep? Had last night cured his nighttime restlessness? The thought of what he had gone through in that horrible prison made her sick. But it also made her feel protective of him. It was an unfamiliar sensation, this feeling of wanting to protect a man. And a highly charged, very dangerous one, she added firmly.

Unable to stand the suspense, Sabrina stifled a small groan of self-ridicule and tossed back the covers. She would only peek around the edge of the door. If he was asleep she could go back to bed and go to sleep herself. It was not knowing how he was faring that was keeping her awake, she decided. If he was out on the balcony again she would *still* return promptly to her own bed! She made that promise to herself as she tiptoed across the room to stand near the door.

Feeling utterly ridiculous but unable to resist, she peered cautiously around the door. Jake was flung in a magnificent sprawl on his stomach, his face turned toward the window, eyes closed. The sheet foamed at his waist and the darkness of his hair was an intriguing note against the crisp white pillow. Sabrina breathed a small sigh of relief. He was asleep.

Which meant that she could stand there in the shadows and study him for a moment or two. The only other time she had seen him totally at rest was this morning, but on that occasion her mind had been bent on escaping. She had barely even glanced at him as she'd fled the balcony. Now she was forced to admit that something deep within her responded to the blatantly sensual picture he made lying there. Her body warmed at the memory of what he had made her feel the night before.

But sex, Sabrina reminded herself grimly, even such passionate, soul-shattering sex, was never enough. And surely sex could be the only thing on a man's mind when he made love to a woman he'd known such a short time. Sex seemed to be the only thing on men's minds regardless of how long they knew a woman!

Sabrina chewed anxiously on her lower lip and then resolutely dropped her hand from the door. She must turn away and get back to her own bed before she succumbed to the inexplicable desire to cross the threshold into Jake's room. Nothing, but nothing would be gained by such a crazy move. And there was so much to lose.

She had taken exactly one pace back toward the safety of her bed when his voice came to her in a soft, gritty drawl out of the darkness.

"Good night, butterfly."

Sabrina fled back to the bed. He'd known she was there all along! He really did have a sixth sense. Something had awakened him, because she was certain he'd been asleep when she padded to the door. Ruefully she slipped back under the covers and pulled them protectively up to her chin. Then she ordered herself to sleep.

The following day passed without incident. Jake behaved himself during the seminar, much to Sabrina's amused relief, but when she congratulated him on the fact afterward he merely smiled cryptically and said it was because she hadn't provoked him. That night Sabrina stoically resisted the urge to peek into his room. The uneasy suspicion that he was lying in his bed, aware of her inner struggle, plagued her until she eventually slept.

The next afternoon Sabrina announced a change of schedule.

"What?" Jake mocked when she told him. "You mean you're not going to load me down like a pack llama with that umbrella and the towels and the books?"

"I want a break from all that sand," she explained loftily.

"I thought you came to Hawaii for the beach!"

"You should be grateful I'm giving you a vacation from playing chief sand-castle-construction engineer. You know damn well all the kids in sight will zero in on you as soon as you appear on the beach!" she chuckled.

"I don't mind the kids." Jake shrugged easily as he commandeered two poolside loungers and arranged them under the shade of a tabletop umbrella. The pool itself was an imaginative creation, fashioned to resemble a tropical stream. It meandered through acres of heavily landscaped grounds, the twists and turns providing a measure of privacy in places.

Sabrina smiled at Jake's comment. "No, you don't mind the kids, do you? When did you discover your flair with children?"

"About eighteen months ago," he said dryly.

"After you escaped? You'd never worked with kids before?" Sabrina was surprised at the information.

"No, I preferred to devote myself to daring escapades. It wasn't until I was more or less forced into a career crisis in that prison that I began assessing my other possible skills."

"It's not a joke!" Sabrina scolded as he finished adjusting the umbrella and sat down beside her.

Jake gave that serious consideration, sitting with his knees drawn up in front of him, his arms resting on top. "No," he finally acknowledged. "It wasn't a joke. This is, in fact, the first time I've ever been even vaguely tempted to make a joke out of it. You're good for me, butterfly. Even if you are making me wait."

Sabrina felt the heat rise in her cheeks at the look he gave her. "I don't want to hear any more on that subject!" she informed him haughtily, squelching a small flicker of pleasure at his words. "Let's go over the topic for tomorrow's discussion." She opened the book she had brought along, ignoring Jake's groan of dismay.

"You mustn't make him spend his whole vacation studying, Sabrina!" Larissa Waverly stood over them, shaking an admonishing finger.

Flaunting, Sabrina decided, taking in the sight of

Larissa's voluptuous figure encased in a swimsuit which was even smaller than the yellow one she herself had on. Where had Larissa appeared from? Sabrina slid a sideways glance at Jake to see if he was noting the display of cleavage.

Jake's face was schooled in his usual polite, rather remote expression as he greeted the other woman. Larissa sat down with languid grace and sipped at the iced drink she held in one hand.

"There's no quiz at the end of the ten days, you know," she confided cheerfully to Jake. "This kind of seminar is strictly for fun. It appeals to people who like to justify their vacations!"

"Do you teach a lot of these vacation seminars?" Sabrina asked curiously.

"One or two a year. The advantage for the instructor, of course, is that his or her way is paid!" Larissa grinned. Then she turned back to Jake. "What do you do for a living, Jake? I know Sabrina, here, is a librarian."

"I teach," he said simply.

"Really? What college?" Larissa asked eagerly.

"I teach little kids," Jake corrected dryly.

"Children!" Larissa seemed rather taken aback. "I would never have guessed."

"He's superb with children," Sabrina heard herself proclaim. "He has an incredible rapport with them."

Jake flicked her a faintly amused glance but before anyone could make a further comment the small group was joined by a fourth member. Perry Dryden wandered up, apparently emboldened by Larissa's presence. He must have decided there was safety in numbers, Sabrina thought.

Jake ignored him with the supreme indifference of a lion for a mouse, so Sabrina tried to cover for her escort's rudeness by including Perry in the conversation. It wasn't hard. Larissa Waverly was happily relating amusing anecdotes which had occurred during other vacation seminars she had conducted.

When she concluded a particularly humorous story that had taken place on a cruise ship the previous summer, she got to her feet. "I feel like a swim. Anyone want to join me?

Sabrina thought the other woman looked rather pointedly at Jake, but he showed himself surprisingly adept at overlooking the obvious invitation. In the small, awkward silence which ensued, it was Perry Dryden who rose nobly to the occasion and did the gallant thing.

"Sounds like a great idea," he said, unbuttoning the bright aloha shirt he was wearing over his narrow swim trunks. It occurred to Sabrina that Perry apparently took excellent care of his body. He looked quite fit for someone who worked in an escrow office. He probably worked out at a health center, as did so many other people these days.

She watched as he carefully wrapped his glasses in the flower-spattered shirt and set the bundle down at the foot of Sabrina's lounger. He smiled with a trace of apology as if he were leaving a small offering. "Would you like to join us, Sabrina?" he tried hopefully.

"I think I'll wait, thanks," she said gently, aware of Jake's silent disapproval. She didn't know why she wasn't deliberately baiting him by accepting Perry's invitation. Somehow that particular game didn't seem worth the candle. The small act of defiance would only elicit an annoying lecture from Jake afterward. At least that was the explanation Sabrina gave herself as she shook her head. It was certainly a more palatable explanation than the other one that came to mind. The less pleasant reason was that she was already subconsciously accepting Jake's claim on her.

Without his glasses Perry didn't look quite so shy and reticent, she thought idly as she watched him stride off beside the tall, elegantly proportioned Larissa. Nor did he appear to be intimidated by the task of escorting one of the most stunning women at the pool.

"I thought they'd never leave," Jake muttered. "Want something to drink?"

"Umm." Sabrina leaned back, one knee bent. "Iced tea sounds good."

He nodded once. "I'll be right back."

An unconscious smile hovered on Sabrina's lips as she watched him glide barefoot to the busy bar at the end of the pool. That masculine grace of his must have been a by-product of his martial-arts training. It showed up in places other than the dance floor. It was there whenever he turned, walked, got to his feet or sat down. And she remembered all too well that it was very much a part of the way he made love. Hastily Sabrina dragged her gaze away from his retreating back.

As she focused on the pool again, her eyes fell on the small bundle at the foot of her lounger. Then, for no reason she could think of, Sabrina found herself leaning down to rummage about in the folded shirt. When her hand closed over the shape of Perry's horn-rimmed glasses, she looked up guiltily.

Perry and Larissa, however, had swum out of sight beneath one of the little bridges which arced across the pool at various points. The sense of guilt increased as Sabrina lifted the glasses free of the shirt and held them up to her own eyes.

Clear glass.

Hastily Sabrina rolled the frames back into the aloha

shirt and replaced the bundle. Clear lenses. Poor Perry. He must feel the horn-rims gave him a more impressive appearance.

It was a shame he was operating under that misconception. His face was really more . . . Sabrina paused in her thoughts, searching for the proper description. More imposing? Striking? Stronger-looking? She gave up. If he wanted to wear clear lenses, that was his concern. Her small bit of curiosity about the matter had now been satisfied.

Jake returned with the iced drinks and Larissa and Perry swam back a short while later. Sabrina gave the little group another fifteen minutes of casual chatter before she decided she'd had enough of watching Larissa display herself in front of Jake. One couldn't help liking the woman, Sabrina realized wryly, and Jake certainly wasn't showing any interest, but enough was enough. Perhaps, like Perry, she was feeling a little intimidated by her own lack of size and stature. Tall people could be very wearing at times.

"Come on, Jake," she ordered firmly, getting to her feet. "I want to buy a muumuu in one of the hotel shops to wear to the luau tonight."

If either Perry or Larissa wondered at the obedient way Jake rose and gathered up the towels and books, they were both too polite to remark on it.

It was Jake who decided to comment upon the casual way she had commanded his obedience. "I get the distinct feeling you could adapt quite readily to playing the courtly lady. Sometimes you have a way about you which puts me in mind of some of the females we've been studying in Larissa's classes," he noted dryly as he followed her along the path toward the hotel lobby.

"It's not often in this day and age that a woman gets a

chance to enjoy the *convenience* of a man who has sworn to serve and obey," she agreed cheerfully.

"I'm sworn to serve, Sabrina," Jake corrected a bit too gently. "The obedience part could get a little shaky if pushed to extremes."

"Feeling henpecked?"

"Henpecked is a description that's usually applied to husbands. I don't qualify, do I?" he retorted coolly.

For some reason that quiet observation took the wind out of her sails. "No," she agreed weakly, "you don't."

Jake didn't look out of place in the hotel boutique with its collection of colorful muumuus, aloha shirts, swimwear and beach clothing. It was the shop which looked a little out of place around him. He had a way of seeming somehow apart from his surroundings, Sabrina thought as she waved him to a chair. He appeared complete and totally self-contained. It was an unusual quality, she realized. If she hadn't learned about the claustrophobic restlessness she would have said he was a man who didn't need anyone or anything.

"Wait right here while I try these on," Sabrina told him cheerfully as she selected half a dozen of the bright muumuus from the rack.

"Yes, ma'am."

When she glanced at him suspiciously he smiled blandly back at her. Frowning, Sabrina hurried into the fitting room.

She was trying on the third muumuu when she finally gave vent to the frustration that had been growing inside her from the time she had tried on the first.

"Damn! I was afraid of this," she muttered aloud.

"What's wrong, Sabrina?" Jake called as the saleswoman hovered anxiously nearby.

"They're all too long! I always have this problem with

off-the-rack clothes unless they're specially designed for my height," she called back through the curtain.

"Perhaps a smaller size?" the saleswoman offered hopefully.

"It might be short enough but it will be too small across the shoulders," Sabrina predicted gloomily.

Jake spoke again. "Come on out and let me see how it looks."

Morosely Sabrina obeyed. The Hawaiian-style dress she had on was a fitted version of the traditionally full muumuu. It was a brilliant splash of red and purple and gold. And it fit perfectly except for the length. Jake eyed the dress speculatively, much to Sabrina's surprise.

"It fits fine except for the hem, right?" he confirmed, circling around her to examine the dress from all sides.

"I love it. Except for the hemline," she sighed. "If I had a sewing kit and if I had time before dinner tonight, I could fix it."

The saleswoman shook her head. "If you can wait until tomorrow, I could have it shortened for you."

"No, thanks. I wanted it for this evening. I should have thought of this yesterday," Sabrina said. "You'd think I'd learn that the world doesn't revolve around people my height. Especially the world of fashion."

"My, we are feeling put upon this afternoon, aren't we?" Jake teased. Sabrina shot him a warning glance but he was already turning to the saleswoman. "How much to find someone this afternoon who could take up the hem?" he inquired calmly.

Sabrina stared at him, astonished. But the saleswoman was doing a quick analysis of the situation. She had rather hoped the client would take the muumuu regardless of the length. After all, few people worried overmuch about the fit of such a casual garment. However, if the client's gentleman escort wished to pay for the alteration, who was she to complain? She quoted him a figure almost at once and Jake nodded.

Sabrina opened her mouth to protest but Jake gave her a gentle push in the direction of the fitting room. "Go change, Sabrina."

When she emerged from the little room he was already paying for the dress. "Jake! You don't have to do this! Please, I'll pay for it."

He smiled at the woman behind the counter and turned away to take Sabrina's arm. "It's already paid for. Let's go. The lady wants to get working on that hemline."

"You shouldn't have done that," she protested quietly as he steered her out of the shop. All she could think about was the state of his finances. Memories of the run-down condition of his school and the limitations of his own wardrobe arose. He had no business buying her expensive muumuus!

"I felt like doing it," he drawled. "I wanted to buy you a present."

"Oh." Nonplussed, Sabrina could think of nothing to say except, "Thank you."

"You're welcome."

Immediately she started wondering what sort of gift one gave a bodyguard when the job was over. A large tip?

The muumuu fit perfectly when it was delivered to Sabrina's room half an hour before the start of the luau. Jake appeared quietly pleased with the total effect when she was dressed for the evening. He nodded in satisfaction and took her arm.

The line of people filing past the buffet table was composed of several members of the seminar as well as other hotel guests. The luau was taking place outdoors in the luscious gardens of the hotel. Traditional foods such as roast pig, lomilomi—a salty concoction of salmon, onion and tomato—and, of course; the infamous poi occupied a place of honor on the buffet table. The hotel kitchens had broadened the appeal of the meal with several other South Seas dishes from other islands.

Sabrina was helping herself to a peppery hot vegetable dish and deliberating over a broiled banana when Larissa Waverly appeared nearby. Jake had finished his selection and was waiting patiently at the far end of the table.

"Hi, Larissa. Don't forget to try some of that pineapple-coconut mousse. I just snitched a bit and it's delicious," Sabrina said politely.

"With your figure you can get away with it. I'm trying to exercise a little discretion or I'll never last the ten days." Larissa smiled. "It must be nice to be so slender and petite!"

Sabrina blinked, realizing that the woman genuinely meant the compliment. "And here I was thinking how nice it must be not to have everything shortened!"

Larissa grinned cheerfully. "I guess it's human nature not to be satisfied with anything in this world. Although your friend Jake seems quite satisfied with you," she added, arching one eyebrow in Jake's general direction.

"I beg your pardon?"

"Come on, Sabrina. That man has eyes only for you. It's incredible, really. The only time there's a genuine smile on his face or real pleasure in those gray eyes is when he's looking at you. All the rest of us mortals get that cool, polite, don't-come-too-close look! As far as I can tell, you're the only one he really cares about communicating with." She helped herself to a bean-sprout salad.

"Larissa, I don't really understand . . ." Sabrina mumbled awkwardly.

"But it's so obvious!" the other woman exclaimed in

rueful tones. "Why, even that argument he launched the other morning in class . . ." she began.

"What about it?"

"He wasn't arguing with the class or with me. Jake was arguing with you. He didn't give a damn about the intellectual side of the question. He was communicating directly with you. A most unusual man."

"He is that!" Sabrina felt a little stunned by Larissa's perspective on the situation. She had seen Jake's polite mask turned to the rest of the world, of course, from the first day she had met him. Only the children and herself had been exempt. But she hadn't realized how obvious it might be to others. It made Sabrina feel uneasy; she began to feel as if fate were conspiring against her.

When she approached Jake a few minutes later carrying her loaded plate, he gave her an odd look. "Something wrong?" he inquired politely.

"Heavens no! Why do you ask?" She plopped her plate down at the small table he had been guarding.

"Just a wild hunch," he murmured cryptically. "Are you going to eat that broiled banana?"

Sabrina glanced down at it, frowning. "No, I don't think so."

"Good. I love them." He reached across and removed the fruit from her plate.

Sabrina watched the skewered banana disappear and wondered what else besides broiled bananas Jake had ever loved.

The luau progressed to the entertainment portion of the evening, featuring the heavy beat of Tahitian dance music and the softer, gently provocative sway of the Hawaiian hula. Sabrina and Jake sat together in the darkness, watching the events onstage. Somewhere in the middle of the Hawaiian wedding song Perry Dryden appeared at the far edge of the crowd. Sabrina idly wondered why she hadn't noticed him earlier. Then her attention was captured by the announcement that volunteers from the audience were needed. The entertainers were going to teach them the hula.

"That sounds like fun!" Sabrina started to get to her feet, only to have her wrist captured by Jake, who yanked her immediately back down onto her seat.

"Sit down, butterfly," he growled. "I'm not having you make a spectacle of yourself."

She started to protest furiously and then noticed that Larissa Waverly was one of those volunteering. With a sigh of resignation Sabrina decided that perhaps she didn't want to find herself onstage next to that beautifully proportioned body. She ceased her struggles.

A few minutes later she was secretly grateful for Jake's interference. The crowd had consumed a fair amount of alcohol by now and the catcalls and whistles which ensued as several ladies learned the hula were not amusing. Jake lifted a lazy, I-told-you-so eyebrow at Sabrina, who made a face at him in return.

"Don't look so pleased with yourself," she stated grandly. "I'm not about to publicly admit you were right."

He grinned. "Just so long as you yourself know it, I'm satisfied." He got to his feet. "Come on, Sabrina. Let's go back to the room. I've had enough for this evening."

Reluctantly she decided he was probably right. Still, it was a shame to end the evening so early. It wasn't even midnight. "Want to go for a walk on the beach?" she suggested as they left the garden area.

"That would be a little reckless, I think," he responded, shaking his head.

"Why? Because you might not be able to resist kissing me?" she dared.

"I was more concerned about the fact that being alone

on an empty beach at midnight might be going out of our way to provide someone with an easy target," he explained.

Sabrina went red, and was suddenly grateful for the shadows that hid her embarrassment. "It's ridiculous, you know, Jake. No one's going to come after me," she grumbled.

"If they do, they won't find you wandering around a dark beach at midnight," he countered. "I'll see to that."

At the door of her room she waited as he fitted the key into the lock. She was still considering various other excuses for lengthening the evening and wondering why she wanted the evening lengthened when Jake pushed open the door. Without being told, she waited the minute or so it took him to wander through her room. When he walked through the connecting door into his own room, she stepped into hers.

"Damn!"

The muffled oath from the other room caught Sabrina midway through a yawn. "Jake?" She went to the connecting door and glanced around the edge to find him down on one knee in front of his canvas tote bag. "Something wrong?"

He didn't turn his head to glance at her; his whole concentration was fixed on the bag in front of him. "My room's been searched, Sabrina."

"Searched! Really?" Fascinated, she stepped through the door. There was something new in the atmosphere. Something hard and dangerous, but it didn't stem from Jake's astonishing announcement. It stemmed from the man himself. Sabrina found herself staring at his crouching figure.

When he rose smoothly to his feet and swung around to confront her she found herself swallowing uncomfortably. This was a side of Jake she hadn't yet seen. Quite suddenly she could understand why Teague had told her mother that Jake Devlin was qualified to protect Sabrina.

He was definitely not a man you'd want as an enemy. Better by far to have him on your side. Sabrina felt a rush of satisfaction at the knowledge that he was, indeed, on her side. There was a controlled violence, a deep-sea chill in those gray eyes that sent a tremor through her, even though she told herself she needn't fear him. Every line of his hard face was set in grim determination. His lean, menacing body had the taut power of a hunting wolf. This was a man who had trouble sleeping at night?

"Sabrina, it was my room that was searched. That means whoever did it already knows who you are. He was trying to find out who I am and how much of a threat I might be. We've got trouble, and my money's on Dryden as a possible source of that trouble. I'm going to call Teague."

"You think Dryden followed us here to the hotel?" she managed, startled as he sat down on the edge of the bed and reached for the phone.

"Dryden's been showing an awful lot of interest in you, Sabrina, and you've got to admit it was a hell of a coincidence that he traveled to Hawaii a few rows behind us on the same plane. Furthermore, there's something about the way he moves when he's not consciously playing the self-effacing escrow officer. I don't like it."

"You've been prejudiced against him from the start!"

"Damn right. The man doesn't know anything more about medieval history than I do. You've heard him in class. He never has anything new or original to contribute. He just takes what someone else has said and phrases it a little differently."

"I had no idea you were paying such close attention," Sabrina muttered scathingly.

"You'll also notice he was rather late joining the luau

tonight? What, exactly, did he say to you that afternoon on the beach when I was helping the kids build that sand castle?"

"He tried to find out more about you," Sabrina admitted with a groan of disgust.

"Figures. Did you tell him anything?" Jake asked grimly.

"Of course not! Who would want to admit she's being trailed around by a professional bodyguard? It's tacky!" Sabrina hesitated, remembering. "I don't suppose this is a good time to mention that Perry's glasses are fake?"

"What the hell . . . ?" He stopped dialing and pinned her with a glance. "Fake?"

She nodded uncomfortably. "It's probably nothing. I mean, he might wear them for effect, you know. I just happened to notice this afternoon when he went swimming."

"Quite the little detective, aren't you?" He half-smiled. She thought there was a note of genuine admiration in his words.

"Well, as long as we're looking for viable candidates for the role of bad guy, I'd like to offer Larissa Waverly. She was pretty damn curious about you, herself. Remember?"

"I remember, but I think we can dismiss her from the picture," Jake stated with assurance.

"Why? Just because she's tall and built like a movie star?" Sabrina asked waspishly.

Astonishingly the edge of Jake's mouth lifted with suppressed amusement. "No, because she's going to be too easy to trace. After all, she's been scheduled to give this seminar for almost a year. And she was at the luau the whole time tonight."

"Details!"

But Jake was already dialing again and in a very short

time he began talking to someone else at the other end of the line in Los Angeles. Sabrina frowned at the cool sound of authority in his voice.

"I don't give a damn where he is. He has a car phone, doesn't he? And he wears one of those crazy beepers. Find him."

It seemed only a minute or two before Teague was, indeed, found. Jake greeted him without any preamble. "Someone's onto us here in Hawaii. Yeah, I've got one possibility. If it doesn't check out, we'll have to start on the hotel guest list. The guy I've got in mind, however, should be someone we can pin down one way or the other fairly quickly." He rattled off the description of Perry in surprisingly minute detail as well as everything else he knew about the man. "I think he's the most logical possibility at the moment. When can you get that information back to me?"

There was a brief silence and then Sabrina winced as Jake exploded very softly. "Like noon tomorrow? Like hell! I want whatever you can dig up tonight. Like two hours from now!" There was another pause and then in a flat, unequivocal voice he said, "Get it for me, Teague. Two hours is all the time I'm going to allow on this one."

Jake hung up the phone with an awesomely quiet click and continued to sit staring thoughtfully out the window into the night.

Sabrina waited expectantly, unwilling to break in on his private thoughts, but at last she could stand the suspense no longer. "Well, Jake? What's happening? What are we going to do now?"

"The search was very professional, Sabrina," he said slowly. "Not the work of a bunch of crazies who don't have any idea of what they're doing. Nothing was disturbed except the strand of hair I'd placed over the lock of my bag."

"Good grief!"

"Which raises some interesting possibilities," he went on musingly. "Up until now Teague has had to assume that the threats were coming from a very unprofessional radical fringe group." Jake broke off and turned to look at her with a hard, unreadable expression. "Go take a nap, Sabrina. We've got a two-hour wait ahead of us. We're safe enough here in the room. The locks on the inside are sound and I think any attempt to grab you will be made out in the open. Probably on one of the side trips you've signed us up for. Maybe the one to the volcano."

"Take a nap! Are you kidding? With all this excitement going on?" she yelped.

"Go lie down," he repeated, getting to his feet. "You're going to need some rest."

All of a sudden he was towering over her.

"Typical of a tall person to use his height to intimidate a smaller one!" Sabrina snapped before spinning around on her heel and heading back to her own room. She slammed the connecting door behind her with savage emphasis.

8

The connecting door was opened by Jake less than fifteen minutes later. Sabrina was standing out on her balcony, the lights off in the room behind her. She remained staring out at the moonlit sea with a brooding gaze even though she sensed him moving toward her.

"I take it you're not going to do as you're told and take a nap?" he observed laconically.

"Of course I'm not going to settle down like a five-year-old and take a nap! How could you possibly expect me to be sleepy under these circumstances?" She refused to turn around.

"Are you angry at me, butterfly?" he asked softly, coming soundlessly forward to stand directly behind her. "I'm sorry if I was a little abrupt a few minutes ago." He didn't touch her but Sabrina could feel his presence mere inches away.

"Are you really worried about the possibility of someone watching us, Jake? Couldn't that hair on your lock have slipped off by itself? I couldn't see anything out of order in your room," Sabrina pointed out dubiously. "Maybe you're overreacting to the situation."

"Take my word for it, Sabrina, I know what I'm doing," he said dryly.

"And your friend Teague? Does he know what he's doing? Is my mother safe?"

"He's good. One of the best. Your mother is in excellent hands."

"Is he good enough to find out something about Perry Dryden in only a couple of hours?"

"That remains to be seen."

"Why did Teague jump when you told him to jump?" Sabrina continued to gaze broodingly out into the distance as she considered the way Jake had issued orders to the man for whom he supposedly was working.

Jake said nothing and Sabrina went on curiously. "Who gives orders to whom?"

After another minute of contemplative silence Jake finally spoke. "I'm afraid Teague is under the illusion that he owes me a favor."

"What kind of favor?"

"Are you always so curious?" Jake drawled.

Only about you, Sabrina answered silently. You see, Jake, I have a horrible suspicion I'm falling in love with you. That's what's really scaring me tonight.

But she couldn't say such things aloud. She could barely bring herself to acknowledge it silently. Sabrina stared straight ahead into the moonlit darkness and realized she had never been so frightened in her life. "You can't blame me for being a little curious under the circumstances," she managed shakily.

"No, I suppose not," he sighed. "Teague figures he owes me something because he was the one who was originally scheduled to make that last gold run, Sabrina.

Something else came up at the last minute and he was pulled off the operation. It was turned over to me."

"Oh, my God!" Sabrina went very still, her hand clenching tightly around the iron railing. For an instant she hated the unknown Teague. If he had made the run that night in that horrid little country, Jake would never have had to go through that hellish experience in prison.

"My sweet Sabrina," Jake whispered on a note of gentle humor. "Are you feeling sorry for me again?" He touched her shoulder and felt the rigidity of her body.

"No, I'm not!" she flung back spiritedly, vividly aware of the feel of his fingers so light and tantalizing on her bare skin. "But I certainly agree with Teague. He owes you one hell of a favor!"

"No, he doesn't. It was all a matter of luck that night. Bad luck. But I'll admit I'm taking advantage of his guilt feelings this evening to prod him into getting me some quick answers."

"For my sake?" she breathed.

"For both our sakes. I'd go crazy if I let anything happen to you, butterfly, don't you realize that?" The hand on her shoulder moved to the curve of her throat in the softest of caresses. Sabrina trembled and her fingers closed even more tightly around the iron railing.

"Oh, Jake!"

"You're shivering, sweetheart," he murmured, bending his head to inhale the fragrance of her hair. "Don't be afraid. I'll take care of you." Now his thumb moved to the nape of her neck and Sabrina wanted to wrench herself away from the rail and throw herself into his arms. Dear God! She really was in love with this man! The experience was totally different from anything she had known before in her life. It left her feeling weak and helpless and vulnerable: all the emotions she had vowed never again to experience.

Tonight those emotions were more powerful than she could possibly have guessed. But they were different, too. Tonight they were accompanied by unexpected strength. It was as if being vulnerable didn't matter so much with Jake Devlin. The risks were worth it. And that knowledge gave her the curious underlying feminine strength she was feeling. Sabrina's lashes closed and she found herself leaning her head back against Jake's shoulder.

His arms came around her waist from behind and he tugged her back against the hard line of his body. "Are you afraid, Sabrina?" he prodded gently.

"No, I'm not afraid." She knew he was asking now about her feelings toward him, not toward the potentially dangerous circumstances in which they found themselves. "I'm . . . I'm just wary. Cautious. Careful. Oh, Jake, I'm *terrified!*"

Spinning around in his arms, she buried her face against the fabric of his shirt with a muted little cry.

"Ah, sweetheart," he soothed, his hands moving now on her spine with infinite tenderness. She could have sworn he was trembling a bit himself. "Can't you trust me a little? I've trusted you so much. I've told you things I've never told another human being. If you give me your trust, I'll honor it just as you've honored mine."

She clung to him, aware that she was stepping over a brink she had vowed to avoid. If she was wrong this time, she knew the results would be unbelievably traumatic. This man had come to mean more to her in a matter of days than anyone else she had ever known. Gingerly, with a heart full of love, Sabrina pushed herself over the edge.

"I trust you, Jake," she whispered. Someday soon, when the time was right, she would tell him that what she really meant was that she loved him. For now, this was all he wanted.

And, indeed, her careful words seemed more than enough to satisfy Jake. He gathered her to him, bending his head to breathe husky assurances into her ear.

"Sweetheart! My charming, maddening, infinitely appealing little butterfly. I know you find me annoying and unimaginative when it comes to things like the Arthurian romances and holding down a job as bodyguard, but I swear I'll take care of you! Just trust me, Sabrina."

"Yes, Jake."

He gathered her closer and then the words he had been uttering faded into kisses, kisses that began as soft, reassuring, caressing things and then evolved into so much more. Sabrina felt the building passion in him and sensed his desire to master it.

But as the kisses moved from the fragrant mass of her hair to her ear and then journeyed slowly toward her mouth, she knew that Jake's willpower wasn't going to be enough on this occasion.

"We've got a couple of hours," he growled. "We're safe enough here in the room. Sabrina, I need you so! I've been wanting you all day. Does it matter any longer, butterfly? Must I go on waiting for you?"

"No, Jake," she whispered, giving him the only answer she could. How could she deny him? "No, Jake, it doesn't matter. Oh, Jake, I want you, too!"

"Don't sound so astounded," he managed with a husky little laugh. "I promise you're going to grow very accustomed to passion!" And then he found her mouth with his own in a slow, burning kiss.

Perhaps it was the danger that seemed to be closing in around them; perhaps it was the fact that she had accepted her feelings toward Jake. Whatever the reason,

Sabrina experienced a strange sense of urgency as she surrendered to his lovemaking. Part of that urgency emanated from him, she realized. Both of them seemed to feel a need to seal their new, fragile understanding.

Her mouth flowered open at his insistent sensual demand. Willingly Sabrina let him drink the honey he found behind her lips and when he deepened the intimacy of the kiss with the thrust of his tongue she felt her own desire quicken. With an aching deliberation he pressed her to him, fitting his palms to the curve of her buttocks. Sabrina moaned into his mouth when he arched her against the blatant hardness of his body.

Without breaking the pulsing contact of their lips, Jake swung her up into his arms and carried her into the darkened bedroom.

"You go to my head, butterfly," he rasped as he set her crosswise on the bed and came down beside her. "You have the power to make me forget everything except how much I need you."

"Do I, Jake?" Sabrina whispered dreamily as she lay with her head pillowed on his arm. Slowly, tantalizingly she lifted her fingers to trail them through the darkness of his hair.

For answer he renewed the passionate kiss he had begun out on the balcony, simultaneously finding the zipper of her muumuu with his free hand. Sabrina made no protest as the colorful garment parted and then was slipped off, to be dropped on the floor beside the bed. Her unconfined breasts seemed to swell with the expectancy of his touch, but Jake undressed her completely before allowing himself to tease the hardening nipples.

Fumbling with the buttons of his shirt, Sabrina made a shaky start at removing his clothing, but in the end Jake pulled away for a moment to finish the task. Standing beside the bed, he kicked off his jeans and the soft suede shoes and then he simply stood staring down at her as she lay in a pool of moonlight.

While he drank his fill of her, Sabrina watched him through heavy-lidded eyes. To her quivering senses he seemed quite perfect. A hard, lean male animal, capable of power and gentleness. It was an intoxicating combination.

"You're beautiful," she whispered wonderingly.

"No," he denied softly. "Around you I feel a little awkward, a little slow, a little dull. You're the beautiful one, butterfly. All color and animation, and when you're in my arms you make me feel beautiful, too."

"Come and be beautiful with me," she invited throatily, holding up her arms.

He came down to her, covering her body with his own but careful not to complete the final union. Boldly he lay between her legs, letting her feel the waiting hunger in him. Then he leaned down to caress the tips of her small, firm breasts with his tongue. When she cried out with growing desire, he used his teeth very gently.

"Oh, Jake! Darling!" She clutched at his shoulders, arching herself against him. Following the line of his spine with her fingertips, she traced a pattern down to the contour of the hard masculine buttocks and there her nails sank sharply into his skin.

"A butterfly with claws," he growled on a note of deep passion. He used his knees to widen the opening between her legs and then he let his palm glide down her stomach to the dark triangle at the apex of her thighs. Sabrina moaned and twisted her hips as the delicious tension coiled more tightly.

When his fingers prowled slowly through the thicket, seeking the intimate goal, Sabrina thought she would melt with the intensity of the feelings flowing through her. Jake's lips covered hers just as he found the most sensitive of places on her body. Instantly she felt as if she were a bowstring which had just been tightened several notches.

"Please, Jake, please!"

"That's all I want to do, sweetheart. Please you." He nuzzled the curve of her shoulder. "Tell me what you like."

"Everything, anything! You seem to know exactly how to touch me," she gasped, raining small, urgent kisses along the line of his throat.

"Just as you seem to know exactly how to touch me," he murmured. He slipped a hand down the softness of her inner thigh, weaving the magic patterns that seemed to set her afire.

Sabrina responded instinctively, writhing beneath him, using her fingertips to explore every inch of his body. Deliberately he trapped her ankles with his own, holding them wide apart. Slowly, with infinite care he eased himself close to the threshold of her femininity.

"Now can you tell me what you want?" he coaxed, doing something indescribable to the pit of her stomach.

"I want *you!*" she managed raggedly, aware of the velvet-sheathed hardness of him so close and so incredibly promising. She knew now just how far that promise went. After the other night her body had learned well the lesson of excitement. It was all bound up with this one man, inseparable from him.

He made a sound of husky satisfaction. "That will do, I think. God, but you're perfect for me, butterfly!" Jake's teeth closed gently on the skin of her shoulder as he mastered her body with great thoroughness. Slowly, deliberately he locked them together, filling her with himself until Sabrina thought her already spinning senses would go completely out of control.

Mindlessly she clung to him, obeying the rhythm he established. It tightened the coiling tension within her until she thought she would burst. Jake seemed to cover her completely, his weight a heavy, binding net against which there could be no resistance. Sabrina lost herself in the folds of that net, surrendering to the power of it. And in the process she conquered it.

"Sabrina!" Jake's muttered cry was fraught with his own sexual tension. He moved his hands under her hips, lifting her more tightly against him and using his sensitive fingers to find the most exquisitely delicate places.

Sabrina's toes clenched, her eyes squeezed shut and her whole body seemed to hit some final level of tension. Jake must have felt it at once. He whispered dark, blatantly sensual words in her ear and inserted his thumb between their bodies.

She was never quite certain what he did then, but everything seemed to explode around Sabrina.

"Jake! Oh, my God! *Jake!*"

He let the quivering vibrations tremble wildly through her and his own body was caught in her response. Almost immediately he was following her over the edge of ecstasy into a shimmering, glittering world of sensation. Sabrina held on to him tightly as they fell through the clouds together.

It was a long time before Sabrina floated free of the cobwebs which had cradled her descent from the heights of passion. When at last she managed to open her eyes, she found Jake watching her. He still lay along her body, trapping her between his arms, and when her eyes met his she thought the gray depths had never seemed warmer or more inviting.

His hard mouth crooked indulgently as she looked up at him. "I don't seem to have much self-control around you," he murmured, giving his head a mild negative shake. "Of all the times to seduce me! Here I am waiting for a crucial phone call, my room has just been searched by a party or parties unknown and I should be carefully plotting out a course of action. Instead I'm in bed with a butterfly."

"It's not my fault." Sabrina smiled with loving wickedness.

"Ah, but it is," he countered. "And the worst of it is, we should be entitled to spend the rest of the night talking about how much you trust me and how beautifully you flutter in my arms. Instead we have to wait for Teague's call and then make some plans."

He rolled to one side, entwining his fingers with hers as he stretched out lazily beside her and stared up at the ceiling. "Sabrina, we have so much to talk about," he said very seriously.

"Do we?" Did he want to talk about something more than mere trust? Did he want to talk about love?

"Yes. A whole future. And there's no time tonight. No time." He exhaled slowly, closing his eyes for a moment and then opening them to continue staring at the darkened ceiling. "I should never have let myself go tonight."

Frowning uncertainly, Sabrina inched closer. "You said we had two hours," she reminded him dubiously.

His mouth curved wryly. "I was desperate for an excuse that would allow me to make love to you. A desperate man doesn't have to search far." Jake sat up abruptly, the effects of the sensual aftermath falling away from him like a sheet. "Up you go, woman!" he ordered briskly, slapping her bare thigh with a possessiveness that Sabrina wasn't sure how to take. "We're going to take a shower and then pack while we wait for Teague's call."

"Pack! Why on earth should we pack?"

"Because my instincts tell me that we should leave here tonight. I'll call downstairs and have the front desk line up a rental car."

"But, Jake!" Sabrina bounced to her knees as Jake got up off the bed with a smooth, easy movement.

"No arguments, sweetheart," he said flatly, bending down to brush a kiss against the tip of her nose. "Just do as you're told, hmmm? I'm the one getting paid to make the important decisions around here, remember?"

There was softness in his eyes as he gazed down at her questioning upturned face, but there was no softness in the rest of him. He was clearly intent on taking command and Sabrina wasn't at all sure how to stop him. When he reached down and snagged her wrist, dragging her gently off the bed and toward the bathroom, she tried to regain some control over the situation.

"You said we were safe in the room, Jake. I don't see why we have to go chasing off into the night! Besides, we don't even know what's going on around here yet. I still think you could be mistaken about your room being searched. One little misplaced hair is hardly sufficient evidence! And there's Larissa's class tomorrow! I don't want to miss it. This seminar vacation wasn't exactly cheap, you know."

"We'll talk about it later," he promised, turning on the taps in the huge shower and stepping beneath the spray. Firmly he tugged her in behind him. "In the meantime, just do as you said you would: trust me."

There was no further chance to argue. Jake lathered himself and then her with quick, efficient movements, rinsing off first. "Your turn," he informed her, stepping out of the shower and leaving her to finish. "Take your time. I've got to get on the phone."

A little resentfully Sabrina stood under the pulsating

water and wondered what had happened to the romantic atmosphere of the evening. "Just like a man to stop being romantic after he's gotten what he wants," she muttered grimly.

The shower door snapped open and Jake stood there, a towel wrapped around his hips. "I heard that." But there was a gleaming challenge in his eyes.

"So?" she dared.

He took a step forward, leaning into the shower to kiss her wet lips soundly. "Just remember that I never promised you romance, sweetheart. I couldn't. I know absolutely nothing about romance. But you're mine now and I am promising to take care of you. When this is all over, butterfly, I'm going to come and live with you, did you know that?"

She stared at him, openmouthed. "Y-you are?"

The shower door closed before she could demand further explanations. A second later the bathroom door closed, too. Sabrina was left alone with the running water and Jake's kiss on her mouth.

Deliberately she dragged out the shower as long as possible. Telling herself she needed time to think, she dawdled under the hot water for a long time, emerging at last to dry herself slowly.

Move in with her? Just like that?

Well, what had she been expecting? A proposal of marriage?

The truth was, Sabrina decided, she hadn't done any advance thinking on the issue at all. Everything seemed to have happened so suddenly, leaving her feeling disoriented and uncertain. What made matters doubly annoying was that Jake seemed eminently sure of himself. She had given him her promise of trust and that was all he seemed to need.

He was right about one thing, she told herself as she

wrapped the towel around herself and stepped back into her room: they needed to do some talking!

"You have the most fascinating way of glaring at a man," Jake announced as she opened the bathroom door.

Sabrina blinked at the sight of him heaving his canvas bag on top of her bed. Her own suitcases were already there, open and waiting. "What are you doing?"

"What does it look like I'm doing? Getting ready to leave. I'll get my things out of the bathroom and then I'll be finished. Hurry up and get dressed, Sabrina. I have a hunch it's going to take you longer to pack then it does me!"

He didn't wait for her response. Turning, he headed back through the connecting door, en route to his bathroom. Sabrina eyed his retreating figure narrowly. Jake was already dressed and shoving his wallet into his back pocket.

He was just passing the edge of his bed when the phone on the small table rang shrilly. Immediately he grabbed for it, moving just out of Sabrina's sight.

"Right on time, pal," she heard him say briskly. "What have you got?"

In the ensuing silence Sabrina moved closer to her bed to pick up the jeans which had been set out for her. She was stepping into the white panties which she found lying conveniently on top of the jeans when her gaze fell on the still-open duffel bag Jake had left behind.

It was, she later decided, probably the same feminine curiosity that had made her examine Perry's glasses earlier that day that now impelled her to glance inside the unzipped bag. Or perhaps it was more personal than that. Perhaps it was only the ancient desire of a woman to know everything there was to know about the man who had claimed her.

In any event she found herself looking down into a collection of neatly folded clothing; on top of one plaid shirt lay an odd-looking belt and a worn leather wallet.

It was the wallet that caught her eye. Jake had been shoving his wallet into his pocket as he'd left her room a minute ago. Why in the world would he carry two of them? This second one looked far from empty. It had that well-used, somewhat stuffed look which implied a variety of credit cards, identification and some cash.

Unable to help herself, Sabrina leaned down and flipped open the leather case. At once the driver's license inside was revealed. The picture was a few years old but it was definitely Jake.

The problem was that the name under the photograph was Jason Stone.

Even as she tried to take in the significance of what she had found, Jake's soft, gritty voice was coming from the next room in the form of a savage oath. Her fingers froze on the wallet as she listened to the remainder of the conversation.

"What the hell do you think I'm going to do with information like that? Stick around here? Of course I'm going to get her away from the hotel!" There was a pause while Teague said something on the other end of the line, and then Jake growled furiously, "Not a chance, Teague. She's my responsibility. I'll handle this the way I think best. And right now I think the best course of action is to get her out of range. We don't know what we're dealing with yet. . . . What's that? . . . You're crazy, Teague. This isn't like the good old days, you know." Jake's voice was as cutting as a knife now. "You take care of things on your end and I'll deal with them here. Just leave Sabrina to me."

The call was terminated abruptly. So abruptly that it

caught Sabrina totally off guard. She was still standing with the wallet in her hand, her eyes wide and disbelieving, as Jake appeared in the connecting doorway.

He took in the picture she made standing there with the towel wrapped around her, her hair in disarray, the offending wallet in her nerveless fingers. And she realized he was coldly furious.

"Been doing a little more detective work, Sabrina?" Gliding forward, he removed the leather billfold from her hand and dropped it back into the duffel bag. Then the chilling gray of his eyes slid over her like a glacier. "Get dressed. Don't waste another single second, woman, do you hear me? I want you dressed and ready to leave in five minutes."

For an instant she almost turned away to obey without question. Jake had turned into a wholly dangerous, wholly intimidating male, not a reasonable, polite escort. Sabrina realized that she was very frightened, and that knowledge gave her the courage to attempt a protest.

"Jake, I think you owe me an explanation," she began in a surprisingly steady voice.

"Later," he interrupted shortly, reaching down to pick up her jeans. "You're going to have to trust me, Sabrina. Just like you said you would. *Get dressed.*"

Uncertainly, her resolution fading under the impact of his grim determination, Sabrina pulled on her jeans. As the towel fell away, she turned her back to him and shrugged quickly into a small-collared western-style shirt. When she swung back, buttoning the front of the shirt, it was to see him pulling the odd-looking belt out of the duffel bag.

"What are you doing?" she whispered.

"I'm getting dressed, what does it look like I'm doing?" He buckled the flat black fastening of the braided cord belt and then strode from the room, clearly intent on retrieving the toilet articles he'd been after when the phone rang.

Sabrina found herself looking at the front door of her hotel room. It came to her that perhaps she ought to be escaping through that door. Everything was falling apart. Jake had become another man, cold and hard and frightening. And perhaps he really was another man. There was that wallet carrying identification which matched nothing he had told her about himself.

She'd had a chance to look at the address on the driver's license. It was for someplace in California, not Portland, Oregon. She thought about the starkness of the apartment in which he had been living. Was it so stark because he didn't really live there? Just how long had he been teaching self-defense to children?

The children. Sabrina took a deep breath, remembering the way Jake smiled at the children. And at her.

Only he wasn't smiling tonight. Since the conversation with the mysterious Teague, Jake Devlin had changed into a hard-faced man who clearly was not about to brook a trace of defiance.

All he wanted from her was trust.

Trust was, Sabrina decided as he came back through the connecting door, the most reckless gift she could have given him. It was the most reckless gift a woman could give any man. She'd trusted her father and he'd abandoned her. She'd trusted her ex-husband and he'd cheated on her.

Jake Devlin was asking her to trust him with her life.

9

‌〰〰〰〰〰〰〰〰〰

*T*he wallet!

Damn! Why had he been so stupid about the wallet? Jake mentally chastised himself as he stepped around Sabrina, tossed his razor into the bag and zipped it shut. Now there was no time to explain, no time to talk about old habits and how hard they died. Dammit to hell!

"Let's go, Sabrina," he ordered gruffly. "I want you away from here."

"Why the big rush, Jake?" she demanded, standing in front of him with her feet braced slightly apart and her hands on her hips. "What did Teague have to say? Why have you got two names? What the hell is going on?"

He looked at her for a second, something about her stubborn stance reminding him of the first time he had encountered her. She could be so sweet and gentle one moment, feisty and haughty the next. Fascinating. But now was not the time to be fascinated. He had a job to do, and to do it he had to maintain control over himself and over her. Their lives might depend on how well he managed his unpredictable client.

"Sabrina, I will explain everything when we've got time. But we don't have time. Come on, butterfly, the front desk said the car will be waiting downstairs."

"If you think I'm just going to run blithely off into the night with you without any word of explanation," she began challengingly, "you can think again!"

Jake sucked in his breath. Sometimes there wasn't time to do things in a chivalrous manner. Had those medieval knights ever had to resort to force and intimidation when trying to rescue a courtly lady?

Deliberately he swung the canvas straps of his duffel bag over one shoulder and reached down to scoop up one of Sabrina's suitcases, not the one full of books. That would have to be left behind. Then he stepped forward to grasp his butterfly by the nape of her lovely neck.

"Let's go, Sabrina."

Sabrina gasped resentfully as his fingers found the cluster of nerves at the vulnerable nape. He wasn't hurting her, Jake reminded himself grimly, but he had to admit there was now an element of coercion involved. She would find it almost impossible to resist the delicate pressure he was applying. Her body must sense the threat of great discomfort which awaited should she dig in her heels and try to fight.

"Let go of me, Jake!" Sabrina hissed furiously as he propelled her firmly toward the door. "I'll go with you, but if you don't stop using your unscrupulous martial-arts tricks on me, I swear I'll scream all the way through the lobby!"

"I'm sorry, Sabrina," Jake muttered, dropping his hand from her neck but watching her warily as she moved ahead of him through the hotel door.

"Every time you apologize I get more nervous!"

"Not as nervous as I am," he shot back dryly.

She glanced back at him, her brows drawn severely together. "Why, Jake? Why are you suddenly acting as if time has run out?"

He shook his head, unable to find the words to explain the instincts that had flared to life in him this evening. "I just have a feeling, Sabrina," he said as they walked swiftly down the corridor.

"What kind of feeling?"

"The kind I had the night I made that last gold run," he retorted without stopping to think. "The feeling that everything is deteriorating rapidly and that something has been gravely miscalculated. *That's* the kind of feeling I've got. Now, will you kindly move a little faster?" Deliberately he closed the short distance between them, urging her more quickly down the stairs to the front desk.

The car was waiting, a silly-looking excursion Jeep with a fringed top and no windows except in front. And no speed, Jake reminded himself with a silent oath as he accepted the keys from the clerk, who was staring curiously. "Was this the only thing you had?" Jake asked.

"I'm afraid so, sir. This is about the only kind of car available for rental and it *was* fairly short notice," the clerk added pointedly.

"I think it's kind of cute," Sabrina said as Jake pushed her outside and into the waiting tourist Jeep.

Jake stared at her for a split second as he slammed the door on her side. "Cute?" he repeated faintly. In spite of himself, he felt a rush of wry amusement. "Only you could find this thing cute, Sabrina. It's slow and exposed and about as subtle as that little yellow bikini of yours."

But she hadn't made a scene as they went through the lobby, he thought in relief as he loped around to the driver's side and slid into the Jeep. She was grouchy and complaining and not very pleased with him at the moment but she wasn't in a panic about going out into the night alone with him. She could have screamed bloody murder at the front desk and then what would he have done? He started the Jeep and shifted into gear before she could have second thoughts.

"Okay, Jake," Sabrina yelled above the roar of the wind as the little Jeep went racing down the narrow road that followed the shoreline. "Now tell me what's going on. What, exactly, did Teague have to say?"

He didn't look at her, his whole concentration on his driving. "Nothing."

"Nothing! And for nothing you spirit me away in the night like this?" she shouted disbelievingly.

"Nothing can mean one hell of a lot, Sabrina," he growled back above the wind, automatically checking the rearview mirror. "A man like Dryden should have left a nice normal trail. Teague couldn't find anything, not even his name on the airline passenger list. There's no record of him working for that escrow company in Portland, either. Teague's digging deeper but we're not going to sit around like a couple of ducks waiting for someone to take potshots." *In spite of what Teague suggested,* he added under his breath.

"Where are we going?" she persisted.

"Hilo. We're going to catch a flight back to the mainland," he answered shortly. What was that little hitch in the engine? Had he felt it or heard it?

"Jake, I think you're making mountains out of molehills," Sabrina informed him grimly. "Furthermore, you owe me an explanation about yourself. Now, I've been very cooperative, considering your somewhat weird behavior this evening. I think you'll have to admit—"

"Shut up," he ordered crisply. Dammit! That *was* a glitch he'd heard in the engine. Of all the incredible bad luck. Perhaps it was something in the gas. Something that would soon be gone? Or had the Jeep been sabotaged?

"Don't tell me to shut up, Jake!" Sabrina stormed. "I've about had it with you tonight. I've been more than a little patient and I . . ." She broke off as the Jeep's engine indisputably coughed. "What's wrong?"

"Everything," Jake groaned. He glanced again into the rearview mirror. The engine was dying, there was no doubt about it, and engines that inconveniently died when one was trying to conveniently disappear were highly suspect. "Sabrina, listen to me," he growled as he surrendered to the inevitable and braked the Jeep to a halt beside the road. As soon as the engine had coughed one last time, he turned in the seat to face his client. She was staring at him, wide-eyed and alarmed. Jake's hand balled into a fist as it lay along the steering wheel. There was no time to comfort her or explain. Every instinct he possessed was screaming now.

"Jake?" she whispered shakily, sitting very still.

"We're going to leave the Jeep and start back to the hotel. We're only a couple of miles from it and there's no place nearer to go for help." He made himself speak slowly, steadily, leaving no room for the thousand and one questions he knew she wanted to ask. Answering questions now could be fatal. "We're not going to walk back along the road. We'll stick to the shoreline, using the rocks and cliffs as cover, do you understand? I don't want you running out, waving down help from any car that might happen past. You're to stick close to me and do exactly as I tell you."

Everything about him was hard and implacable and Jake knew it. He also knew that if he showed any sign of softness or patience now Sabrina would grab for the opening and use it to demand explanations and reassurances. He had none to give.

"Jake?" she whispered softly, searching his harshly set face.

"Right. Let's get moving. Leave everything behind." He swung open the small door on his side and started around to hers. She was already opening it reluctantly as he grabbed for the handle.

"Jake, I don't think . . ." she began nervously as she slipped out to stand in front of him.

His fingers closed around her shoulders and he gave her a swift, meaningful shake. "Sabrina, I don't want any arguments, questions or demands for explanations. You will do as I say tonight and fire me as your bodyguard later, is that clear?"

"It's clear, all right," she gritted, stepping away from him. "And that's exactly what I'm going to do when you've finished acting like an idiot tonight! Fire you!"

"Fine. We'll discuss severance pay later. Get moving." He captured her wrist and tugged her toward the sheltering shadows of the moonlit cliffs along the ocean. The crash of the surf was an ever-present roar now and he was grateful for it. If worse came to worst, the sound would be excellent cover.

He could have wished for a little less moonlight, he decided as he led Sabrina down a nonexistent path toward the beach. It was relatively easy to see, but that also meant they could be seen. At least they wouldn't be leaving footprints on this rocky surface.

They were out of sight of the road, dropping rapidly down toward the beach, when he heard the sound of another car coming from the direction in which they had come. Jake froze, and Sabrina, who had been watching her footwork on the uneven surface, promptly plowed into him with a muffled curse.

Instantly he wrapped a palm over her mouth to still the question that was on its way. She stood stoically imprisoned as he listened to the slowing of the car's engine. It was going to stop.

Which meant that time had run out. Jake turned to scan the rocky outcroppings around them and made his selection. "Not a sound, Sabrina," he growled in her ear as he released her mouth and pulled her toward a cavelike indentation in the cliff wall. She followed him mutely, only her hazel eyes blazing with questions and, he saw for the first time, a trace of fear.

He wanted to take her in his arms and soothe away the fear. He wanted to have her yelling at him, telling him she wasn't going to stand for any more of his high-handed behavior. He wanted, Jake realized, for things to go back to normal. That wasn't a very likely possibility until he took care of the business that had arisen.

The important thing now was to impress upon Sabrina the importance of following orders exactly. How did one give orders to a butterfly? Jake wondered unhappily as he propelled her into the mouth of the small cave and pushed her back behind the cover of some huge rocks. She wasn't pleased with what was happening but at least she hadn't rebelled yet. He crouched down beside her and cupped her face between his palms.

"Sabrina, I'm going to have to leave you here while I take care of Dryden."

"Perry? He's in that other car?" she gasped.

"Probably. If not him, then someone else equally unpleasant."

"I don't want you going out to face some criminal, Jake!" she whispered, stricken.

"Sweetheart, I have to find him before he finds us," Jake said patiently. "But I want you to give me your word of honor you'll stay in this cave until I come back for you. You're not to move so much as a wing tip, do you understand?"

"No," she grated, lifting her chin.

"Sabrina, I mean it."

"I don't want you going after whoever it is alone, Jake!"

"Dammit, woman! In this business it's not smart to wait to be found. I prefer to do the hunting! You're to stay here and keep under cover until I'm finished. I'm going to have enough to worry about without wondering where the hell you are when the shooting starts!"

Sabrina went white, her face a pale image against the dark rocks. "Shooting?" she repeated in a horrified tone.

He should have kept his mouth shut, Jake realized belatedly. Now he'd only added fuel to the flames. He drew in a steadying breath, his hands tightening around her face. "There is every possibility that whoever is out there is armed. I can take care of myself, Sabrina, but not if I have to worry about you, too. Give me your word you'll stay put here in this cave!"

The tip of her tongue emerged to lick suddenly dry lips and her eyes were pools of shadows. Shadows he couldn't read, Jake acknowledged. "I'll stay here as long as I think I should," she temporized in a sober tone.

Jake throttled back his anger. "I think, when this is all over, butterfly, I may beat you. Severely." He rose to his feet. "Stay put, Sabrina. Unless you want to get me killed."

"No!"

It was, he decided, the one and only effective argument he'd found. He'd better use it for all it was worth.

"That's exactly what's likely to happen if you start running around out there."

Sabrina closed her eyes in pain and then opened them to watch as he casually unfastened the black metal buckle of the strange belt he'd looped around the waistband of his jeans. He transferred the object to his neck as she said quietly, "All right, Jake. I'll give you my word."

He hid his sigh of relief. It wasn't himself he'd been worrying about; it was her. Stooping down, he gave her a quick, hard kiss and then straightened. There was one more thing that had to be said.

"Sabrina, if I'm not the one who finds you . . ." he began, searching for the right way to say it.

"Oh, Jake!"

"If Dryden finds you," he hurried on quickly, "you're not to put up a fight, do you understand? I'm sure he wants you alive. You stand a better chance if you don't argue or run. Do as he says. Teague will be coming after you when he realizes what's happened. He's good, Sabrina. Just do as Dryden orders until Teague can handle him."

There was no point hanging around after that. Jake slipped silently out of the cave, his soft suede shoes making no noise on the rocks. He hadn't gone more than a few paces when Dryden's voice yelled out from somewhere along the cliffs. He wasn't in sight. Probably still down by the cars, Jake thought.

"Sabrina! Sabrina, can you hear me?" Dryden pitched the call above the surf.

Jake flattened himself against the wall of the cliff, glancing back into the mouth of the cave. He could barely see her sitting there behind the rock, her knees pulled to her chest and her arms wrapped around them. She stared back at him as Perry Dryden yelled again into the night.

"Sabrina, listen to me. You're in great danger. The man you've been traveling with isn't who he says he is." Perry spaced each word out so that it would reach as far as possible into the surrounding countryside. "His real name is Jason Stone. And he's a killer. A hired mercenary who's been assigned to kidnap you when his client gives the signal. Can you hear me, Sabrina?"

Jake remained where he was, palms flattened to the wall of rock behind him, his gaze locked with Sabrina's. My God! What was she thinking? About the wallet? That Jason Stone I.D.? What else could be going through her mind but that? He could read nothing from her shadowed expression, could barely see her at all, in fact. He hadn't a snowball's chance in hell of explaining that wallet now. Dryden was using his earlier discovery of the wallet to advantage.

How far did a woman's trust extend when the man who was asking for it had known her such a short time?

"Sabrina!" Dryden's voice called out again, closer this time. He must have been making his way along the cliffs. "Sabrina, I don't think he's armed. If he hasn't got a gun, use any chance you get to run out into the open. I'll cover you."

Sabrina sat unmoving, staring out past the sheltering rocks at Jake. He felt trapped. If she chose to believe Dryden and bolted for the open beach, he probably wouldn't be able to stop her before the other man saw her. Jake waited in aching uncertainty for some sign. If only he'd known her longer so that she had more reason to trust him. If only he'd had a chance to explain that wallet. If only.

Tonight all the arguments were in Dryden's favor. That wallet was the most damning one of all. Dryden had seen it, of course, when he'd searched the room. He was taking a chance that Sabrina might be persuaded to flee from cover if he could scare her thoroughly enough about one Jake Devlin.

What had he, Jake, done to warrant Sabrina's trust tonight? It seemed like he'd spent the entire time of their acquaintance either lecturing her or trying to intimidate her into obeying. Or making love to her. Why should any woman trust a man who had such a limited repertoire and who carried around second sets of identification?

She'd liked Perry Dryden from the beginning. He was the right size for her, she'd implied. A pleasant man who had the manners of one of those mythical medieval knights. A man who had seemed content to admire her from afar. Unlike himself, Jake thought, gritting his teeth silently. Oh, no. *He'd* pushed her into bed at every opportunity. Would she interpret that as evidence that he'd taken advantage of her? Damn Dryden and damn the whole mess. He felt so helpless at that moment.

As helpless as he'd ever felt in that horror of a prison.

And then Sabrina lifted her hand in the darkness and blew him a soft butterfly kiss.

Jake felt as if the prison door had swung open. The rush of relief which went through him was totally inde-scribable. Slowly he unstuck himself from the wall of stone, his gaze still meshed with hers. She was smiling at him! He couldn't believe his eyes for a few seconds. Silently she mouthed three words.

I trust you? Or *I love you?* He couldn't be sure which. But did it really matter? With a woman like this, it must amount to the same thing. Jake could think of nothing to do, no way to express his gratitude. There was no time. With a quick nod that probably seemed curt, he melted away from the mouth of the cave, heading back along the rocks in the direction of Perry Dryden's voice.

First things first. He'd been hired to do a job but he felt as if he'd just been sent out on a quest. All he lacked was the heavy armor and a charger. He did, however, have the first requisite: a lady to be rescued.

Old habits did, indeed, die hard. The silence with which he moved toward his goal was proof enough of that. The supple suede shoes didn't dislodge so much as a pebble as Jake worked his way back toward where the Jeep had been left. Having searched his luggage, Dryden would know he didn't have a gun.

Dryden called out a few more times, urging Sabrina to run to him for protection, but he'd apparently decided that things weren't going to work out quite that easily. By the time Jake lowered himself to a flat outcropping from which he could see the Jeep, Dryden had given up yelling at Sabrina.

The car parked beside the tourist Jeep was a Ford. Dryden had apparently searched the Jeep and was now intent on making his way down to the beach. Knowing he was the only one carrying a gun had probably given him added courage, Jake decided wryly as the smaller man bounded down the cliffs toward the beach. The weapon in his hand flashed briefly in the moonlight and it was no Saturday-night special. It was very large and very mean-looking. Guns were such an unaesthetic form of defense and destruction, Jake decided critically.

Although, he had to admit, they did have their uses. If he'd brought along a gun tonight he could have taken out Dryden as the other man stood silhouetted against the pale beach. It was fortunate, though, that Dryden had searched the room and come to the conclusion that Jake was unarmed. It might put him off his guard, make him careless.

Slowly Jake prowled along the top of the cliff, watching his quarry on the sand below. Dryden was searching the face of the rock in front of him, looking for some sign as to which direction Sabrina and Jake had gone. He'd know they weren't on the road above because he hadn't passed them, and he'd know that the closest outpost of civilization was the hotel.

Jake waited impatiently for Dryden to put two and two together and realize that it was reasonable to assume he and Sabrina had started back in the direction of the resort. At last the man on the beach made his decision. He started walking parallel to the water, pointing his gun toward the cliffs. Then he apparently decided to have another try at the psychological approach.

"I'm only after the woman, Stone or Devlin or whoever you are. Send her out and you can disappear. Come on, man, she's not worth getting killed for, is she? Send her out onto the beach. I'll take her away in the car and you can walk back to the hotel. We'll pretend nothing ever happened, hmmm?"

His voice kept on, promising safety if Jake would give him Sabrina. Jake ignored the words, staying in the shadows of the rocks as he kept pace with the man below. What he needed was one good solid opportunity. He slipped the corded weapon from around his throat and held it coiled in one hand. It would be best if he could wait until Dryden edged in a little closer to the cliff face.

Jake's eyes narrowed as he realized how close the man was to the pocket in the cliff where Sabrina was hiding. *Sabrina, my sweet butterfly,* he thought, *don't move so much as an eyelash.* Would Dryden see the deeper shadow which was the cave opening?

If opportunity wasn't going to come knocking, he might have to make his own, Jake decided, picking up a large rock in one hand. Crouching on one knee behind the shelter of a convenient boulder of hardened lava, he hurled the object in his hand toward a section of the cliff that was in the opposite direction from Sabrina's cave. It landed with a faint clatter that could barely be heard above the crash of the surf.

It was enough of a sound, however, to send Dryden into a professional gunman's stance, both hands anchoring the weapon as he fired three times in rapid succession.

It was the best chance he was going to get, Jake knew. Without hesitation he sent the heavy-buckled cord spinning through the air. The black, ropy thong struck the outstretched wrists of the other man and the metal ends snapped back on themselves exactly as they had been designed to do, twining tightly around his wrists. The impact on Dryden was dramatic. The gun dropped from his suddenly nerveless hands as the corded weapon momentarily cut off all feeling, and he yelped in startled rage.

Jake was on him before Dryden realized what had happened, hurtling down the face of the cliff and across the sand with the sleek speed of a pouncing cat. Once he got his hands on Dryden, everything became very unequal in a hurry. The smaller man fell to his knees and then sprawled unconscious on his back as Jake went through the motions of his art with a kind of deadly grace. It was all over in less than a minute.

"Jake!"

Sabrina stood in the cave entrance staring at the tableau on the sand. Jake was poised above the unmoving body of his victim, looking as if he would very much like to have Dryden stir even an inch just for the pleasure of sending the fallen man back into unconsciousness.

Jake's dark head snapped around as Sabrina emerged from her hiding place. "Following orders in your usual haphazard fashion, I see," he observed dryly. "Didn't I tell you to stay put until I told you it was safe to come out?"

But he was smiling at her, Sabrina realized as she glared at him. The relief flowing through Jake was almost palpable. "When this is all over," she informed him haughtily, "we're going to have a long talk about the high-handed, chauvinistic manner in which you order me around, Jake Devlin. How many times do I have to remind you that you work for me, not vice versa!"

Then she was running toward him, stumbling through the sand and into his arms. As they closed around her she buried her face against his chest. "Oh, my God, Jake, I was so scared when I heard those shots." She pounded her small fists against him. "I've never been so frightened in my life. I was terrified something had happened to you! Don't you ever put me through that sort of thing again! Do you understand?"

"Yes, ma'am," he whispered huskily, cradling her warm, slender body close. "I hear you." And then for sixty seconds he allowed himself the luxury of just holding her close.

When he pushed her gently away a moment later, Sabrina looked up into his face questioningly. "Now what? Do we take Perry to the police?"

"In a little while," he agreed distantly, glancing down at the man at his feet. "In a little while."

Sabrina stared at him. "What do you mean? We've got to take him to the cops and phone Teague, don't we?"

"We need some answers first, Sabrina."

"Answers?" She frowned, not liking the cool, cryptic way in which he was talking. She also didn't care for the hard, remote expression on his face as he studied the silent man on the beach. "Jake? What are you going to do?"

"Go back to the Jeep and wait for me, Sabrina."

"I'm not going anywhere again until *I* get some answers! What are you going to do to Perry?"

"Find out what Teague needs to know," Jake replied wearily. "Go back to the Jeep, sweetheart. I'll be along in a few minutes."

"Jake! I don't want you torturing that man or anything!" Sabrina suddenly felt vastly uneasy.

"There won't be a mark on him," Jake promised dryly. "Go on, Sabrina."

Frustrated beyond measure, Sabrina stamped one foot in the sand. "You are the most infuriating man, Jake Devlin!" Then she whirled and raced for the cliff.

She didn't stop to glance back when she reached the top, merely kept going until she was out of sight of whatever was happening on the beach. Flinging herself into the front seat of the Jeep, she sat with her arms folded tightly across her breasts and glared at the instrument panel.

Life, she reflected moodily, had grown enormously complicated since she had met Jake Devlin. Then she gave a long, shuddering sigh of relief. Jake was safe. And so was she.

10

~~~~~~~~~~~~~~~~~

In an extremely short period of time after the events on the beach, Sabrina found herself pacing the floor of her hotel room. She was not in the best of moods.

A grim and near-silent Jake had emerged with a dazed-looking Perry Dryden about fifteen minutes after Sabrina had been sent back to the car to wait. She had flicked an assessing glance over Dryden as he was tumbled, bound, into the backseat of the Ford, but except for a strangely exhausted and sullen expression on his once pleasant features, he appeared unharmed.

Jake, on the other hand, wore an expression of grim satisfaction. Sabrina decided as he slid into the passenger seat and switched on the ignition that she would not inquire too closely into how he had gotten the information he wanted from Perry Dryden.

"You don't have to eye me as if you thought I worked part-time in the bottom of a dungeon," was all Jake said in a rather mild tone as he swung the car back onto the road and started it toward the hotel. "He was willing enough to talk when I explained a few facts to him. He's not a wild-eyed radical. He's a professional who was hired by some wild-eyed radicals. He's not about to do anything chivalrous and heroic like go to jail on their behalf for the sake of a cause."

"Not even a misguided knight-errant, huh?" Sabrina sighed in resignation. "I'm very disappointed in you, Perry," she added, glancing into the backseat.

Dryden didn't appear concerned about her opinion. He sat gazing stoically out the window.

Nothing more was said en route to the hotel. Jake's mind seemed to be fixed on other matters, Perry wasn't at all talkative, and so Sabrina had to wait with gathering impatience for the short trip to end. When they pulled into the hotel parking lot, Jake dispatched her to her room.

"I have to call the cops, and Teague and I have to keep an eye on Dryden until someone arrives to take him off my hands. Go on up to the room, Sabrina. I'll be along when I can."

She drew a deep breath. "No," she said simply. "I'm tired of taking orders from you, Jake Devlin. I have a few questions of my own that I want answered and I want to see what happens when the cops arrive. This is about the most exciting thing that's ever happened to me, you know!"

"It is?" He looked unimpressed as he walked his prisoner toward the lobby. "I certainly hope you don't intend to maintain this level of excitement now that you've experienced it. I personally prefer a quieter life-style."

She thought about what he had said earlier in the

evening when he told her he planned to move in with her and for no apparent reason smiled brilliantly.

In the end, however, she had wound up climbing the stairs to her room shortly after the police arrived. Jake had phoned Teague and had then informed Sabrina that her mother would be trying to get in touch.

"You'd better go to the room and wait for her call," he advised innocently.

"You're just trying to get rid of me," she complained, watching as the police began to walk into the lobby.

"You've had your fun," Jake told her bluntly, moving to stand in her line of vision. "Now, move, woman! I want to handle the cops by myself."

Sabrina had been vastly annoyed but there was something about the determination of his stance which made her groan in surrender. Baring her teeth at him briefly, she spun around on one heel and started for the stairs.

Which was how she came to find herself pacing the floor of her hotel room.

Never again, she promised herself, was she going to take orders from Jake Devlin. She'd had enough of hired bodyguards! She was repeating that to herself several times when the phone rang. Sabrina pounced on it, sitting down on the bed with her feet up.

"Hi, Mom!" she greeted the caller enthusiastically. "How are things at your end?"

"Sabrina, are you okay?" Mrs. McAllaster's worried voice came with urgent question. "Mr. Teague tells me you were with your bodyguard tonight when that man Dryden attacked. He said Dryden apparently had bribed the front-desk clerk there at the hotel to keep him informed of your movements so he knew when Jake rented the car. Apparently he then put something in the gas tank and followed you."

"I'm perfectly fine. What else did Teague say? I've been having trouble getting answers at this end. My bodyguard is choosing to play the strong, silent type."

"Just that Dryden turned out to be a professional hired gun. Someone who does things like this for pay. The group which was threatening my company hired him to kidnap you. Then they were going to put pressure on me and the firm to halt all work on the government contract."

"But what good would that have done? Even if your company gave in to the pressure, the contract would eventually have been completed, if not by your firm, then by another," Sabrina pointed out logically.

"Publicity. The impact of an act of terrorism. Who knows what goes through the minds of such people? Heaven knows there are enough of them in the world today, though. Teague says Dryden talked to your bodyguard, giving him enough names to enable the FBI to pick up the ringleaders. Sounds as if everything's going to be cleared up very quickly. I was certainly worried there for a time. I'm so glad I didn't let you talk me out of assigning someone to look after you!" Mrs. McAllaster concluded with a sigh of relief.

"Yes, well, I've been meaning to speak to you about that," Sabrina informed her grandly just as the door to her room swung open, revealing Jake. Her eyes met his as he slowly closed the door behind him. "This bodyguard you hired has been taking his job a little too seriously, Mother."

"Well, thank heaven he did!" her mother exclaimed in heartfelt tones.

Jake crossed the floor and sank down onto the foot of the bed. There was a wary expression in his cool gray eyes as he watched Sabrina.

"You don't quite understand, Mom," Sabrina went on

patiently. "He's got this annoying habit of giving orders whenever he thinks he knows best. He insisted on sleeping on my couch at the apartment in Portland. He made sure we had connecting hotel rooms here in Hawaii and he gets up in the middle of the night . . ." She broke off as Jake's eyes narrowed. "He gets up in the middle of the night and opens the connecting door," she continued sweetly. "He doesn't approve of the way I drive. I believe he considers me frivolous and scatter-brained and he treats me accordingly. And he spends a great deal of his time lecturing me! He does all this and then claims he has the right to do it because you hired him!"

"I see," Mrs. McAllaster said thoughtfully. "What, exactly, do you expect me to do about it?"

"I want you to tell him in no uncertain terms that he's fired!"

As if he'd heard enough, Jake reached for the phone, removing it from Sabrina's fingers with a swift little movement that left her hand tingling. She frowned and wriggled her fingers experimentally, wondering exactly what he'd done. That was another accusation she'd forgotten to make during the conversation with her mother. Jake seemed to have no compunction about using his more subtle martial-arts techniques on her.

"Hello, Mrs. McAllaster," he said in very formal tones. When Sabrina lifted her head he was still watching her intently. "Yes, I understand. . . . No. No. . . . Yes. Thank you. . . . Yes, of course." A slightly longer pause followed and then Jake said carefully, "I shall look forward to meeting you, too. And don't worry about Sabrina. I'll be taking care of her. Good night, Mrs. McAllaster. . . . What's that? . . . Oh." He smiled briefly. "Yes, I'll be working without pay. Good-bye." He handed the phone back to Sabrina.

"What did she say?" Sabrina demanded, dropping the receiver carelessly.

"She said," Jake spoke slowly, "that I was fired."

"Ah hah!" Sabrina's eyes gleamed with satisfaction and inner humor. "So now we're on equal footing!"

"She also pointed out that the hotel room was paid for through the end of the seminar," he went on smoothly. "And that I was welcome to finish the ten days in Hawaii. A sort of bonus for having saved her charming daughter's neck."

Sabrina thought about that. "Well, I suppose that's fair enough. Are you enjoying the seminar, Jake?"

"Oh, enormously," he said soberly.

"Very educational, isn't it?" Why was she suddenly feeling a little nervous?

"I've learned a great deal. But not as much as I learned out there on that beach tonight," he told her bluntly.

Sabrina blinked. "You mean about Dryden and his friends?"

He shook his head. "I mean about you."

She tilted her head to one side, experiencing a strange sense of uncertainty. The amusement went out of her hazel eyes. "What did you learn about me, Jake?"

"That you trusted me. You were irritated, angry and consumed with a lot of questions I didn't have time to answer, but you trusted me. When you blew me that kiss from the cave . . ."

"Oh, that," she tried to scoff lightly.

"Did you mean it, Sabrina?" he persisted, not moving from the end of the bed.

"Of course I trusted you," she said brightly, bouncing up off the bed to walk restlessly out onto the balcony. What was he getting at? Why that serious, searching look in his eyes? She remembered distinctly that moment when she had crouched in the cave, staring across the face of rock and listening to Dryden tell her that Jake Devlin was the real source of danger. She'd thought about the wallet and she'd thought about Jake's rather vague background.

And then she'd remembered fixing hot milk for him in the middle of the night. She'd recalled the intensity and warmth of his lovemaking. She'd thought about the way he smiled at children and at her.

But most of all she'd thought about how much she loved him. And then she'd smiled and blown him that little kiss of encouragement. It was all she'd had to give.

"It was like a token," Jake said gently, coming up to stand behind her.

"That little kiss?" she whispered wonderingly. He felt so warm and his presence was so reassuring there behind her. She wanted him to touch her.

"Remember how Larissa explained that the knights always sought a token from their ladies to wear in battle? They claimed it gave them courage and strength to have something from the woman they served."

"I didn't think you put too much stock in those fundamentals of chivalry," Sabrina noted breathlessly.

She could sense the faint smile in his words. "I didn't, not until tonight. Tonight I understood a great deal about them. At least the part about tokens and rescuing one's chosen lady. Sabrina, do you know why your trust meant so much to me tonight?"

"Because it kept me from making an unfortunate mistake and getting myself kidnapped?" she tried to quip.

"No," he declared flatly. "Because I think that with you trust is tied up with love."

Sabrina froze at the railing. Jake's hand descended on her shoulder, spinning her gently around to face him. She searched his face anxiously, knowing he had guessed her secret and not at all certain what he would do with it. Did Jake want love?

"Do you love me, Sabrina? As well as trust me?" he whispered almost harshly. The gray eyes were almost silver in the waning moonlight. They burned with a molten metal glow.

"Yes." The single word was stark and it seemed to leave her unbearably vulnerable, as if she'd shed a suit of armor and now stood naked before him.

A shudder went through him and then Jake was pulling her into his arms, cradling her close against him as if he would never again let her go. "My God, Sabrina! You can't possibly know what that means to me! Don't ever be afraid again, sweetheart. I swear, I'll take care of your love. I'll never give you cause to doubt me, please believe me."

She reveled in that for a full minute and then Sabrina asked gently, "Are you trying to tell me something, too, Jake?"

"You don't have to wonder about how I feel," he confessed heavily, burying his face in her hair. "I think I started falling in love with you that night when you made me hot milk and sat up with me to help me go to sleep. When I woke up and found you still in my arms the next morning, it felt so right. The night I made love to you out on the balcony I knew for certain what was happening to me, even though I'd never experienced anything quite like it before in my life. Later I made myself promise to give you time. I knew you needed it. I wanted you to learn to trust me. Then, tonight, everything started coming apart."

"You mean after I found that wallet?" she mumbled against his chest.

"I can explain about that," he groaned. "But it's a little complicated."

"I had a feeling it might be," she murmured dryly.

"It has to do with old habits and precautions that I learned a long time ago when I lived another kind of life, Sabrina. I used to travel under several different covers. The Jason Stone name was one of them. It had been useful on occasion as a red herring to lead nosy types astray. I just tossed it into the duffel bag when I was packing that morning in my apartment. I didn't have any real plan in mind to use it, I just took it along in case. An old habit. I suppose it occurred to me in a rather vague fashion that it might be helpful if we got into trouble here on the island and had to leave. I might have used it to book passage on the airplane tonight, for example, if we'd made it into Hilo. It would have muddied the trail a bit."

"Why were you so furious when you came in from the other room and found me holding that wallet, Jake?"

"I was furious with Teague when I got off the phone. When I walked in and realized how much explaining I was going to have to do and how little time there was, I was really angry. Mostly at myself, I suppose," he admitted.

"Why were you angry with Teague?" she asked curiously, lifting her head a little and pulling back to meet his eyes.

"Because he had just suggested that since someone was definitely onto us I should stick around the hotel and use you as bait to draw the bad guys out into the open. I could have beaten him to a pulp for that very practical suggestion!"

Sabrina smiled at the faint traces of fury in his expression. "As it turned out, Teague's little plan went into effect anyway. So everyone's happy, hmmm?"

"If you love me, I'm happy," he stipulated. His eyes softened. "My sweet little butterfly. I have so little to give you. It's going to be another year or two before the school is big enough to bring in a good income. I have no right to ask you to marry me—''

"Are you asking me to marry you?" Sabrina interrupted swiftly. "Because I'm accepting!"

A slow, loving grin edged his mouth as he threaded his fingers sensually through her hair. "That doesn't leave me much choice, does it? If you've already accepted, then the only chivalrous thing I can do is go ahead and marry you."

She threw her arms around his neck, eyes soft and dreamy. "I'm going to make you the happiest henpecked husband in the whole world," she vowed.

"Henpecked husband!" he mocked. "I was trying to see myself in the role of chivalrous knight!"

"Same thing," she dismissed blissfully. "Oh, Jake, I do love you so. I didn't think I would ever love a man the way I love you. I didn't think I would ever be able to trust a man again."

"And besides," he added wickedly, "I rather think you were having a good time steering clear of getting emotionally involved, weren't you? Running around in the MG, going to parties, rushing off to crazy seminars being held in exotic locales, handling men as if they had very limited uses. . . ."

"Don't tell me my fast life is coming to an end?"

"Ummm. I think we'll start by getting rid of that little car of yours," Jake decided thoughtfully.

"Over my dead body!"

"Portland has an excellent bus system. You don't need a car. I have one which we can use when we go out of town," he informed her firmly.

Sabrina looked up at him through her lashes. "And my parties and seminars and casual treatment of males?"

"You won't need all those things to keep you busy

now. I'll make sure you're properly entertained," he promised gently.

"Jake, you do remember that Mom just fired you, don't you? You are no longer in a position to give orders," Sabrina explained tauntingly, her eyes laughing up at him.

"I may have lost my rights as paid bodyguard but I have recently acquired a whole bunch of new rights and privileges as a soon-to-be-married man," he assured her, and then she saw the dawning light of passion in his gray gaze. "Sabrina, I love you so! I need you so much."

"To keep away the nighttime ghosts?" she whispered understandingly.

"Not exactly. I need you to put the joy back in my life. I need your warmth close to me at night. I need the passion and the gentleness and the loving concern. Give me everything, sweetheart," he ended raspingly as he swung her off her feet and into his arms. "Give me everything because I need all of you. And in return, I swear you'll have all of me. Forever."

She touched a hand to the side of his cheek and smiled, her face aglow with her love. "Yes, Jake. Everything. Forever."

He lowered his head to kiss her lingeringly, a kiss of promise and love and passion and protection, all mixed together in an inseparable concoction that Sabrina knew now she could trust completely.

When he broke off the tender caress it was to set her lightly on the bed. There he undressed her as if she were a jewel wrapped in velvet. When she lay naked he rose and quickly shed his own clothing, coming back to her with a soft groan of desire and anticipation.

"Take me flying, butterfly. I love to find myself trapped in your wings!" The slow, scorching kisses that he rained on her throat and down to her small breasts made her moan with pleasure. His palms moved across her nipples, rousing them to peaks of desire, and his strong, rough thigh shifted along the inside of her leg, sending little shivers of excitement through her whole body.

"Oh, my darling Jake. I don't know how you do this to me!"

"Do what?" he provoked softly, using his teeth with care on one nipple. "Tell me what I do to you."

"You make me want you so!" she gasped, spearing her fingers through his hair and clutching him to her. "Whenever you make love to me I feel as if I'm going to go out of my head!"

He laughed huskily, his satisfaction plain. "You're so wild and free in my arms!"

Slowly they touched each other, giving and receiving pleasure in generous portions. Sabrina trailed her fingertips across Jake's chest, toying with the flat male nipples, following the line of hair which tapered down to his waist. When she pushed lightly at his shoulder he rolled obediently onto his back, eyes gleaming, as she knelt to explore him completely with her lips and her hands.

It was glorious to have him mutter thickly and arch his hips against the touch of her gentle hands. It gave her a sensation of passion and power when she used her teeth to nip lightly at the skin of his thigh and felt his immediate response. Delicately she trailed the stinging little kisses up along his hip, seeking the most intimate, the most vulnerable, the most responsive places.

Her hands fluttered over him, caressing and playing and provoking until it was clear he could stand no more of the delicious torment. "You've flitted around me long enough," he grated deeply, rising and looming over her to guide her body beneath his. "It's time you came home in my net."

He slid his hands down her body and parted her legs with an urgent but gentle aggression that only served to heighten Sabrina's clamoring senses. Eyes closed, she pulled him down to her and he went willingly, filling her body with his own in a surging movement.

"Jake, oh my love, my love!" she cried out passionately. Her body absorbed the impact of his, enveloping it in softness and warmth.

"I love you," he growled huskily as his mouth closed over hers and his body began the primitive rhythm that led to ecstasy. There were other words after that, dark, passionate words that could sound right only in the depths of sensual excitement. Sabrina reacted to them as she did to his caresses, her whole body responding, twisting, arching.

They sang the wordless, tuneless song together. Sabrina's legs wrapped themselves tightly around Jake's hips and he held her fiercely close as, with one hand, he traced exotic designs down her back and over the erotically sensitive areas that only he seemed to know existed.

When the stirring convulsion rose to take her, Sabrina called out Jake's name over and over again, clinging to him with all her might and reveling in the knowledge that he, too, was caught up in the swirling climax of their passion.

"Sabrina!" His body arched almost violently and he held her as if he would never let go, until the storm of their lovemaking began to settle around them.

Slowly, languidly, feeling in no hurry at all because she had the rest of her life ahead of her, Sabrina came out of the pleasant world of lazy satisfaction to find Jake lying beside her, his head turned on the pillow to watch her. She yawned daintily.

"It's late," Jake murmured irrelevantly, his eyes moving over her with a possessive expression. There was supreme masculine contentment emanating from him.

"Ummm," she agreed, her lashes drooping slightly as she smiled at him. "Sleepy?"

"Yes." He grinned. "I believe I am. Unlike you, I spent the night working."

Her smile broadened as she traced the line of his mouth with her forefinger. "Do you think the claustrophobia feeling will bother you tonight?"

"Not as long as I can reach out and hold you," he drawled with great certainty. "You are a source of unbelievable comfort. When are you going to marry me?"

"As soon as we get back from our honeymoon here in Hawaii," she chuckled happily.

"I'm not sure you've got the sequence of events right," he contradicted. "I think the wedding comes first and then the honeymoon. In the morning I'll call the detective I spoke with tonight and see if he can't arrange for us to be married here in Hawaii."

"You're not worried that we might be rushing things a bit?" Sabrina asked suddenly.

"No." The statement was flat and unequivocal. "Are you?"

"No," she admitted thoughtfully. "I really do feel quite sure about all this. How is that possible, Jake, when we've only known each other such a short time?"

His mouth curved invitingly as he caught hold of her hand and threaded his fingers through hers. "It's simple. You're the butterfly and I'm the guy with the net. We were made for each other."

"Well, I suppose that's a more realistic role for you than trying to maintain the image of a knight-errant serving his lady with a pure love and devotion from afar," she sighed. "You weren't very good at the platonic-love-and-devotion bit."

"I've been telling you all along that when a man feels what I feel for you, he's not likely to be very good at running a courtly, chivalrous love affair."

"I'm not sure you even tried!" she complained good-naturedly, lifting herself up on her elbow to frown ferociously down at him.

"I wanted you too much to play games of chivalry."

Sabrina flopped back down onto the pillow, laughing softly. "So, maybe you weren't too good at the loving-from-afar bit. You were terrific at rescuing damsels in distress."

"And you are terrific at slaying night dragons," he whispered, lifting her hand to his lips and kissing her fingers. "We make a good team, I think."

"Yes. Just remember the operative word is 'team,' though. You're no longer in charge, Jake Devlin. I have a feeling it's going to be tough convincing you of that fact, though," she sighed.

"Just keep in mind how much I love you when you're tempted to lose your temper with me," he advised ingenuously.

"If we're going to discuss the ground rules for this relationship, there's one other point I should bring up," she went on determinedly.

"Yes?"

"You're not to use your sneaky martial-arts techniques on me in order to get your own way, Jake," she instructed firmly.

"Sneaky martial-arts techniques?" he repeated, frowning in polite concern. "You mean things like this?" He moved his fingers lightly across her thigh, finding an exotically sensitive nerve she would never have dreamed existed.

"Exactly like that," she tried to snap waspishly. But her leg had already shifted a little in a small shiver of pleasure.

"Or this?" He moved his hand again, this time along the base of her throat.

"Oh, yes, Jake," she whispered, reaching out to pull his head down to hers. "Like that. Precisely like that!"

And then he kissed her with all the reverence, chivalry and passion of a modern-day knight in shining armor.

Genuine Silhouette sterling silver bookmark for only $15.95!

What a beautiful way to hold your place in your current romance! This genuine sterling silver bookmark, with the distinctive Silhouette symbol in elegant black, measures 1½″ long and 1″ wide. It makes a beautiful gift for yourself, and for every romantic you know! And, at only $15.95 each, including all postage and handling charges, you'll want to order several now, while supplies last.

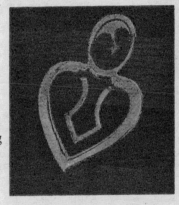

Send your name and address with check or money order for $15.95 per bookmark ordered to
Simon & Schuster Enterprises
120 Brighton Rd., P.O. Box 5020
Clifton, N.J. 07012
Attn: Bookmark

Bookmarks can be ordered pre-paid only. No charges will be accepted. Please allow 4-6 weeks for delivery.

N.Y. State Residents
Please Add Sales Tax